AN INTRODUCTION TO TRANSITION-METAL CHEMISTRY: LIGAND-FIELD THEORY

AN INTRODUCTION TO TRANSITION-METAL CHEMISTRY

LIGAND-FIELD THEORY

LESLIE E. ORGEL

Fellow of Peterhouse
Assistant Director of Research, Dept of Theoretical Chemistry, University of Cambridge

LONDON: METHUEN & CO LTD
NEW YORK: JOHN WILEY & SONS INC

First published October 13, 1960
Reprinted 1961, 1962 and 1963

1.4

Printed in Great Britain by
Butler & Tanner Ltd, London & Frome
Methuen Catalogue number 2/6344/11

Contents

Preface

I have tried to give an account of ligand-field theory which is both short and non-mathematical. In the interests of brevity I have included only a minimum of descriptive chemistry; to avoid mathematical arguments I have often sacrificed precision. The reader is referred particularly to *Theory of Transition-Metal Ions* by J. S. Griffith for mathematical methods, etc. The two books are intended to be complementary.

This book is directed to students of inorganic chemistry and to others seeking a general impression of this rather new field of valency theory; it is not for professional theoretical chemists. References are therefore mainly to review articles, although original sources of important early work and of very recent material which has not yet been reviewed are occasionally given.

The choice of subject matter is largely determined by my own interests, but partly by other circumstances. All topics, however important, which do not lend themselves to qualitative exposition have been excluded. Pauling's valence-bond theory is not described since his own classic writings on the subject make such description unnecessary.

I am indebted to Mr J. S. Griffith, Dr S. F. Kettle and Professor H. C. Longuet-Higgins for many valuable suggestions.

L. E. ORGEL

Peterhouse
Cambridge
July 1959

CHAPTER ONE

Preliminaries

1.1. Introduction

The subject of this book is the elementary theory of the chemistry of the elements from titanium to zinc and of the corresponding elements of the later periods. This is purely a choice of convenience; the elements included form a group which may usefully be treated together.

The peculiar interest of the transition metals is generally agreed to be connected with their ability to form compounds in which the outermost set of five stable *d* electron orbitals is only partially filled. It is the presence of incomplete *d* electron shells which is responsible in one way or another for the varied colours and also for the paramagnetism which many transition-metal compounds display. Furthermore the phenomenon of variable valency which these elements exhibit to a greater extent than any others, except perhaps the actinides, is due, as we shall see, to the unusual relations which exist between the successive *d* electron ionization potentials.

The general approach to the chemistry of the transition metals which we shall use depends to a large extent on the approximation by which we regard a transition-metal compound as made up of individual metal atoms or ions, perturbed by their immediate environment, but interacting only weakly with each other. Our success in explaining quantitatively the experimental facts about various classes of compound is at present in proportion to the adequacy of this approximation. For this reason the metals themselves, their alloys, the interstitial carbides and nitrides, etc., in which the interaction between metal atoms is strong are beyond the scope of the present volume. Our methods are most useful in discussing the more ionic compounds such as the oxides, halides, hydrates and sulphates, and the other compounds which come within the field of coordination chemistry.

1.2. Transition-metal atoms and ions

The first transition series begins after calcium when, for the first time, the 3*d* orbitals become occupied. We shall not consider scandium in any detail for although the free atom has the electron configuration $(3d)^1(4s)^2$ the chemistry of the element is almost restricted to that of the trivalent ion which has the closed shell electronic structure . . . $(3s)^2(3p)^6$.

Throughout the first transition series the energies of the 3*d* and 4*s* orbitals, in the neutral atoms, are very similar. The usual ground state configuration is $(3d)^n(4s)^2$, but the chromium and copper atoms have the configurations $(3d)^5(4s)^1$ and $(3d)^{10}(4s)^1$, respectively. The special stability of the half-filled d^5 shell (Chapter 3) is sufficient to cause the displacement of an electron from the 4*s* into a 3*d* orbital making the lowest state of the configuration $(3d)^5(4s)^1$ more stable than that of the $(3d)^4(4s)^2$ configuration for chromium. Similarly the $(3d)^{10}(4s)^1$ configuration is stabilized relative to the $(3d)^9(4s)^2$ configuration in the copper atom.

The relative energy of different atomic orbitals is not independent of the state of ionization of the atom concerned. As the positive charge on a transition-metal ion increases the $(n-1)$ *d* orbital becomes more stable relative to the *ns* orbital. In the first transition series all of the ions which are met with in the so-called ionic compounds, namely the divalent and multivalent ions and the Cu^+ ion, have ground states corresponding to d^n configurations. Thus we may consider the common transition-metal ions in their 'ionic' compounds as d^n ions, more or less modified by their environment.

In Table 1.2.1 we give the first three ionization potentials of the elements from calcium to zinc. We note first that the second ionization potential of copper is substantially greater than that of any other of these elements. This is the basic reason why the Cu^+ ion is more stable than the monovalent ions of the other transition metals.

Similarly the order of increasing third ionization potential is:

Sc, Ti, V, Fe, Cr, Co, Mn, Ni, Cu, Zn, Ca.

The ease of removal of a third electron accounts for the absence of divalent ionic compounds of Sc^{2+}, while the high third ionization potentials explain the difficulty of oxidizing Ni^{2+} and Cu^{2+} and

TABLE 1.2.1

The ionization potentials of the transition metals of the first series in electron volts

(1 electron volt = 23·05 Kcals.)

	First ionization potential	Second ionization potential	Third ionization potential
Ca	6·11	11·87	51·21
Sc	6·56	12·80	24·75
Ti	6·83	13·57	27·47
V	6·74	14·65	29·31
Cr	6·76	16·49	30·95
Mn	7·43	15·64	33·69
Fe	7·90	16·18	30·64
Co	7·86	17·05	33·49
Ni	7·63	18·15	35·16
Cu	7·72	20·29	36·83
Zn	9·39	17·96	39·70

the absence of compounds of Zn^{3+}. For the most part the ionization potentials of the remaining ions correlate rather closely with the difficulty of oxidizing divalent to trivalent ions in aqueous or similar environments.

The variable valency exhibited by the transition metals is connected with the rather gradual increase of their ionization potentials with ionic charge. The sudden jump between the second and third ionization potentials of calcium should be contrasted with the corresponding changes for the other elements of this period.

Ionization potentials are not the only factor influencing the ease of oxidation of an ion as may be seen from the example of the Co^{2+} and Co^{3+} ions. The data in Table 1.2.1 suggest that the Co^{3+} ion should be rather unstable relative to Co^{2+}, comparable in stability say to Mn^{3+} relative to Mn^{2+}. While this is true for the $[Co(H_2O)_6]^{3+}$ ion, the Co^{3+} ammines are not easily reduced. In fact, with a certain class of ligands which includes the amines, the Co^{3+} ion is made stable in octahedral complexes to an extent which is large enough to compensate for the extra energy needed to ionize a free Co^{2+} ion to the trivalent state (Chapter 5).

1.3. Ligands

We shall understand by the term 'ligand' any ion or molecule which is directly attached to a metal ion and which we regard as bonded to it. The most common types of ligand are monatomic or polyatomic negative ions and neutral polar molecules. The latter molecules are almost always ones which have one or more pairs of unshared electrons, for example NH_3, H_2O and CO. Structure determinations have shown that with very few exceptions polar ligand molecules are oriented so that one unshared pair of electrons points directly at the metal ion. Among the more novel types of ligand are unsaturated hydrocarbons and their radicals, for example acetylenes, olefines, benzene, the cyclopentadienyl radical and the cycloheptatrienyl radical.

A chelating ligand is one containing two or more functional groups so arranged that they can simultaneously occupy positions in the first coordination sphere of the same metal ion. Familiar examples are ethylenediamine, $NH_2.CH_2.CH_2.NH_2$, and the acetylacetonate anion, $[CH_3.CO.CH.CO.CH_3]^-$, each of which can occupy two coordination positions, and the ethylenediamine-tetra-acetate ion $(^-O_2C.CH_2)_2N.CH_2.CH_2.N(CH_2.CO_2{}^-)_2$ which can probably occupy all six coordination positions in an octahedral complex.

Chelating ligands form complexes of greater stability than those formed by molecules containing similar functional groups, but with only one per molecule. Thus ethylenediamine complexes form under conditions which do not permit the formation of appreciable amounts of the complexes of ammonia or of a primary amine.

In a few cases there are special features of the electronic structure, usually connected with conjugation as in the acetylacetonates or phenanthrolines, responsible for the stability of chelated compounds. This, however, is the exception rather than the rule, for usually the extra stability is due to an entropy effect. In the reaction between a metal ion and two independent ligand molecules to form a complex ML_2 the entropy change during the reaction includes a term which allows for the fact that the translational entropy of the two ligands is lost; before the reaction the three molecules involved can move independently, but afterwards they are all obliged to move together. In the corresponding reaction of a chelating molecule the entropy corresponding to the translational freedom of only one molecule is lost, for the two functional groups of the ligand are tied together from the first. This is illustrated in Fig. 1.3.1.

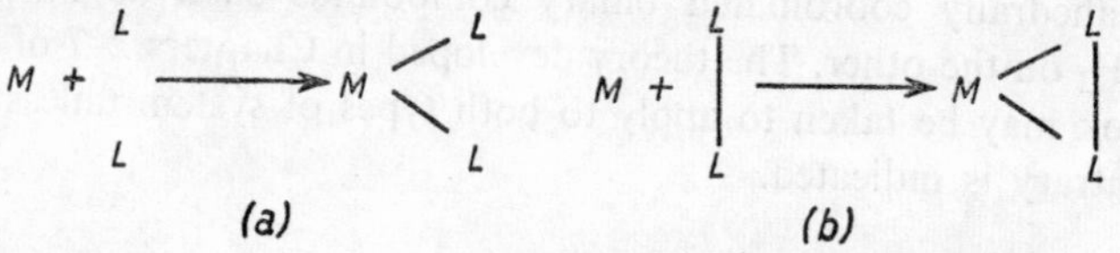

(a) (b)

Fig. 1.3.1. The effect of chelation on the translational entropy change occurring during complex formation. In reaction (a) the translational motion of three independent molecules is replaced by that of a single complex but in (b) only two independent translational motions are possible even before complex formation has taken place

This argument as it stands is a very crude one, for it neglects the many important degrees of freedom other than those of translation. For example the flexibility of the chelating ligand may be decreased when combination with the metal ion occurs. This produces an entropy effect opposing the formation of the complex and tending to decrease the effect of chelation. In a quantitative theory corrections would have to be made for this and many similar effects.

The *additional* stability due to chelation is not very strongly dependent on the stability of the complexes of the simple ligand with the same functional group as the chelating agent, for it depends more on geometric than on electronic factors. This often has surprising consequences, for example the *cis*-glycols are quite good complex-forming agents although simple alcohols show little tendency to form complexes in aqueous solutions.

1.4. Compounds and complexes

It has become customary in descriptive inorganic chemistry to distinguish between the normal compounds of a metal ion and the complexes which it forms. While this distinction may have its uses in classification it does not prove necessary in developing a general theory. The electronic properties of transition-metal compounds are in large measure determined by the nature of the ligands, and only in special cases are they sensitive to the more distant environment of the metal ion. Thus the same theory often applies to a complex cation such as $[Ni(NH_3)_6]^{2+}$ or the corresponding hydrated ion $[Ni(H_2O)_6]^{2+}$, on the one hand, and to octahedrally coordinated binary compounds such as NiO or NiF_2 on the other. The theory developed in Chapters 2–7 of this book may be taken to apply to both types of system unless the contrary is indicated.

1.5. Stability

The word 'stability' is one of the most useful and flexible descriptive terms which we have in inorganic chemistry and probably causes more confusion than any other. I shall try to use it in the sense of thermodynamic stability unless the context makes it quite obvious that I have something else in mind. Thus I shall describe complex ions as labile if I mean that they react readily in solution, but I shall not reject phrases like 'stable in the absence of oxygen', which clearly must refer to the reactivity towards a particular reagent.

The misunderstandings brought about by the ambiguities of the word 'stable' are deeply embedded in our thinking about chemistry. We repeatedly find that progress in the interpretation of chemical properties is hindered if we do not stop to ask, perhaps inelegantly, 'Stable against what?'

1.6. Coordination number and valency

It is difficult to arrive at formal definitions of valency and similar terms which are uniformly applicable throughout chemistry. This is of little importance provided the intended meaning is clear in each particular context. I shall use the term 'coordination number' to describe the number of nearest neighbours bonded to a metal ion and the term 'valency' to describe the formal positive charge on the metal ion. The latter is determined by assigning the usual formal charges to ligands and other parts of the crystal or complex ion which is being considered and finding the formal charge which must be assigned to the metal to achieve charge balance. Thus in NiO we assign two units of negative charge to the oxygen, since it would normally be considered to be present as the O^{2-} ion, and hence we say the metal is divalent. In the $[Mo(CN)_8]^{3-}$ ion we assign one negative charge to each CN group and hence say that the metal is pentavalent.

The valency in this sense is defined only when the formal charges to be associated with each ligand have been decided. Thus in complexes of nitric oxide or oxygen, for which ligands it is not clear that there is a unique, convenient assignment of charge, there is an ambiguity in the valency. We may regard

$$[(NH_3)_5Co—O_2—Co(NH_3)_5]^{4+}$$

either as a Co^{2+} complex containing the O_2 molecule or as a Co^{3+} complex containing the peroxide ion $O_2{}^{2-}$. This need not concern us unduly, for the formal valency of a metal ion in a compound is only very roughly correlated with the charge distribution. We say that the $MnO_4{}^-$ ion is a derivative of heptavalent manganese, but we do not, of course, imply that any entity even vaguely resembling a free Mn^{7+} ion is present. For this reason the occasional ambiguities which arise in assigning the valency of a metal on are of no importance. We are interested in the electronic structure of molecules and this must ultimately be inferred from the experimental evidence, not from our conventional decisions about the assignment of valencies.

CHAPTER TWO

Orbitals and Energies

2.1. The relevant orbitals

The orbitals with which we shall be concerned are labelled *s*, *p* and *d*, following the conventions of atomic spectroscopy. *f* orbitals are important in rare-earth and actinide chemistry, but will not be referred to in any detail in this book. Higher orbitals are happily of little consequence in contemporary theoretical chemistry.

A one-electron wave-function for an atom has the important property that it can be written as a product of a function of the radial distance of the electron from the nucleus with another function which depends only on the angular coordinates of the electron. The former function is relatively simple for a one-electron atom but in all more complicated cases must be evaluated numerically or approximated by an analytical function. The angular functions are independent of the particular atom concerned; there is just one angular distribution for all *s* electrons; three for all sets of *p* electrons; five for all sets of *d* electrons and so on. The classification of orbitals according to their angular functions is essential for any understanding of valency theory, so we shall deal with it first.

The angular dependence of the wave-functions for *s*, *p* and *d* electrons is illustrated in Fig. 2.1.1. The *s* orbital has full spherical symmetry, that is the variation of the wave-function with distance from the nucleus is independent of direction. In the case of *p* and *d* orbitals which have preferred directions in space the situation is somewhat more complicated. There are three different independent *p* orbitals having the same energy. In cases of degeneracy of this sort the choice of orbitals is never unique, for given any acceptable set of three orbitals we may combine them in an infinite number of ways to produce three new, mutually independent, and equally acceptable orbitals. The choice of one particular set is then a matter of convenience and it turns out

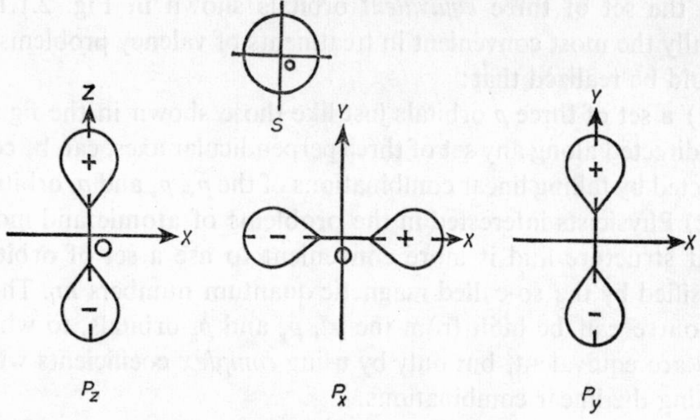

Fig. 2.1.1(a). The s and p orbitals

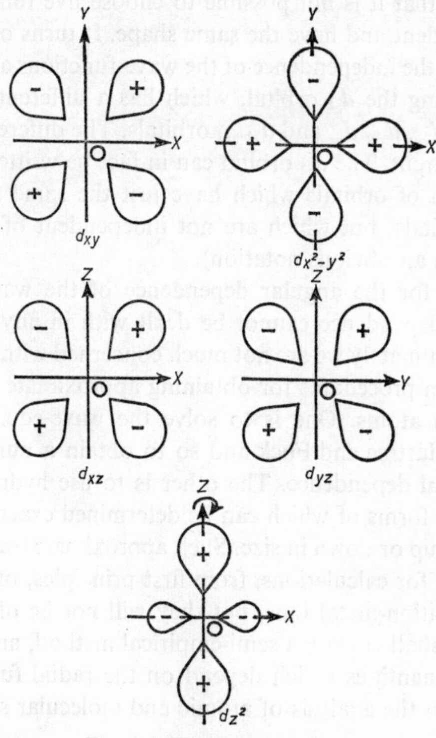

Fig. 2.1.1(b). The d orbitals

that the set of three *equivalent* orbitals shown in Fig. 2.1.1 is usually the most convenient in treatments of valency problems. It should be realized that:

(1) a set of three p orbitals just like those shown in the figure, but directed along any set of three perpendicular axes, can be constructed by taking linear combinations of the p_x, p_y and p_z orbitals.

(2) Physicists interested in the problems of atomic and molecular structure find it more convenient to use a set of orbitals classified by the so-called magnetic quantum numbers m_l. These of course can be built from the p^x, p_y and p_z orbitals, to which they are equivalent, but only by using *complex* coefficients when making the linear combinations.

When we come to the d orbitals the choice of a most suitable set of five real wave-functions is less straightforward. The basic difficulty is that it is not possible to choose five functions which are independent and have the same shape. It turns out to be best to maintain the independence of the wave-functions at the expense of introducing the d_{z^2} orbital, which has a different shape from that of the d_{xy}, d_{xz}, d_{yz} and $d_{x^2-y^2}$ orbitals. The difference however is only apparent. The d_{z^2} orbital can in fact be written as a linear combination of orbitals which have just the same shape as the other d orbitals, but which are not independent of them ($d_{z^2-x^2}$ and $d_{z^2-y^2}$ in an obvious notation).

So much for the angular dependence of the wave-functions. The radial dependence cannot be dealt with in any such simple way, but fortunately we are not much concerned with it. There are two common procedures for obtaining approximate radial wave-functions in atoms. One is to solve the wave-equation by the method of Hartree and Fock and so to obtain a numerical form for the radial dependence. The other is to use hydrogen atomic orbitals, the forms of which can be determined exactly, appropriately scaled up or down in size. Such approximate wave-functions are essential for calculations, from first principles, of the properties of transition-metal ions, but they will not be of importance to us as we shall employ a semi-empirical method, and derive the important quantities which depend on the radial functions of d orbitals from the analysis of atomic and molecular spectra.

The radial wave-functions for a hydrogen-like atom are illustrated in Fig. 2.1.2. It will be noted that only the wave-functions of s electrons

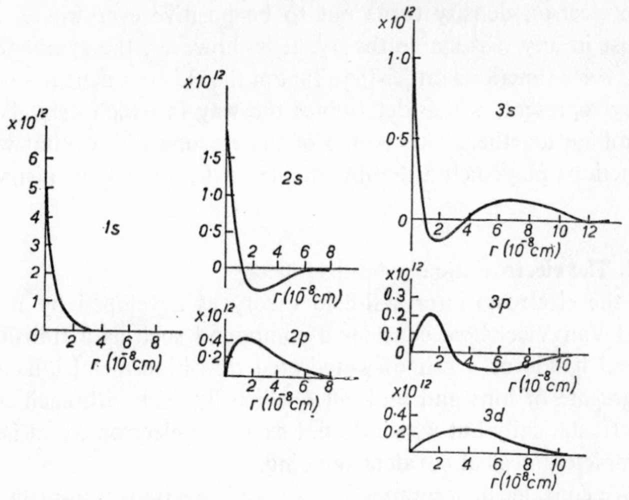

Fig. 2.1.2. Radial wave-functions for hydrogen. Abscissae give distance from the nucleus in A

(After Herzberg, *Atomic Spectra and Atomic Structure*, Dover, 1944.)

are non-zero at the nucleus and that the number of nodes (points where the wave-function changes sign) is zero for the 1*s* function, one for the 2*s* function, two for the 3*s* function and so on. Atomic *p* orbitals have one less radial node than the *s* orbital with the same principal quantum number; *d* orbitals have one less node again.

In Fig. 2.1.3 we show the radial wave-functions of the 3*d* and 4*s* orbitals of a typical transition-metal atom as calculated by the method of Hartree and Fock. The markedly different distributions of the 3*d* and 4*s* orbitals, despite their similar energies, should be noted.

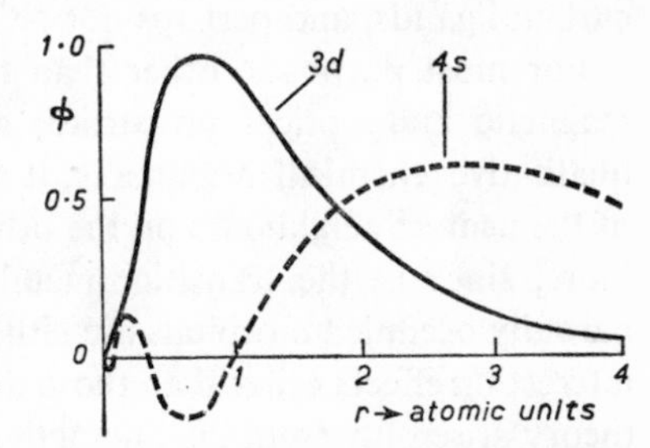

Fig. 2.1.3. Hartree–Fock radial function for neutral manganese (Mn^0, ^6S). *1 atomic unit = 0·5 Å*

(After Hartree, *J. Opt. Soc. America*, **46**, 350 (1956))

We have emphasized the importance of atomic wave-functions. It must be understood that the density distribution for an electron in a given (real) orbital is obtained by squaring the corresponding wave-function. This means that, unlike the wave-function itself, the electron density turns out to be positive everywhere, as it must in any reasonable theory. It is, however, the symmetry of the wave-functions rather than that of the electron densities which they represent, which determines the way in which orbitals can combine together. This is one of the reasons why orbital wave-functions play such a dominant role in theoretical chemistry.

2.2. The electrostatic crystal-field theory

In the electrostatic crystal-field theory as developed by Bethe[1] and Van Vleck[2] we consider a compound such as a transition-metal halide or a salt of a hydrated transition-metal ion as an aggregate of ions and molecules which interact with each other electrostatically but which do not exchange electrons, that is, we completely neglect covalent bonding.

We consider first compounds containing a transition-metal ion surrounded by a regular octahedron of negative ions or of dipolar molecules so arranged that the negative ends of their dipoles are pointed towards the central ion. In addition to many ionic solids, most of the compounds dealt with in classical coordination chemistry are included in this group, for all the common ligands fall into one or other of the classes considered (but not the hydrocarbon ligands, and perhaps not NO, etc.).

For most purposes, other than the detailed interpretation of magnetic and optical properties, and almost certainly for all qualitative chemical arguments, it suffices to consider the effect of the nearest neighbours on the orbitals of a metal ion. Furthermore, since in the transition-metal ions all but the outermost partially occupied *d* orbitals are either filled or completely empty, interesting effects other than those dealt with in the classical ionic theory arise only from the interaction of the electrostatic field of the environment with the *d* electrons.

Consider now the influence of the octahedron of nearest neighbour negative ions or oriented dipoles on the $d_{x^2-y^2}$ and d_{xy} orbitals. Clearly, by symmetry, the ligands along the z axis influence the $d_{x^2-y^2}$ and d_{xy} orbitals to exactly the same extent (Fig. 2.2.1). The situation with respect to the ligands in the xy plane is different for the directions of maximum charge density of the $d_{x^2-y^2}$ orbital point at the ligands along the x and y axes, while those of the d_{xy}

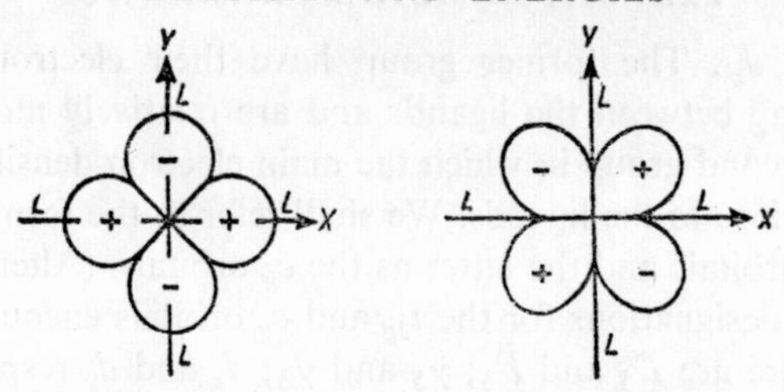

Fig. 2.2.1. The $d_{x^2-y^2}$ and d_{xy} orbitals unequally influenced by ligands on the x and y axes

orbital point along the bisectors of the angles between the bond directions and so maintain a maximum separation from the ligands (Fig. 2.2.1). Since the ligands are always negatively charged or, equivalently, the negative ends of dipoles, it follows that an electron in the $d_{x^2-y^2}$ orbital must be repelled more strongly by the ligands than an electron in the d_{xy} orbital. Thus the influence of the ligands is to destabilize both the $d_{x^2-y^2}$ and the d_{xy} orbital, but the former to a greater extent than the latter.

Consider next the d_{xz} and d_{yz} orbitals. These have just the same spatial orientation relative to the ligands in the *xz* and *yz* planes as the d_{xy} orbital has to the ligands in the *xy* plane. Clearly then they must be degenerate with the d_{xy} orbital. It is not immediately obvious how the energy of the d_{z^2} orbital is related to that of the other *d* orbitals. Since its density is concentrated along the *z* axis and so interacts strongly with the ligands along that axis it is plausible that it, like the $d_{x^2-y^2}$ orbital, is unstable relative to the d_{xy}, d_{xz} and d_{yz} orbitals. Calculations, or group theoretical arguments, confirm this and show that the $d_{x^2-y^2}$ and d_{z^2} orbitals are in fact degenerate in an octahedral environment.

This latter result may seem more plausible if it is realized that the d_{z^2} orbital can be written as the sum of $d_{z^2-x^2}$ and $d_{z^2-y^2}$ orbitals. Each of the latter is obviously equivalent to the $d_{x^2-y^2}$ orbital, and so in fact is their sum. However, this is a dangerous argument because the energy of a linear combination of orbitals is the corresponding combination of the energies only under special conditions.

Our final conclusion, then, is that in a regular octahedral environment the five *d* orbitals split into two groups. One group comprises the three orbitals d_{xy}, d_{xz}, d_{yz} and the other the orbitals

$d_{x^2-y^2}$ and d_{z^2}. The former group have their electron density tucked away between the ligands and are relatively more stable than the second group in which the main electron density is concentrated close to the ligands. We shall refer to the former group as the t_{2g} orbitals and the latter as the e_g orbitals. (Alternate and equivalent designations for the t_{2g} and e_g orbitals encountered in the literature are Γ_5 and Γ_3; γ_5 and γ_3; d_ε and d_γ respectively.)

In Fig. 2.2.2*a* we show the energy-level scheme for the *d* orbitals in an octahedral environment. We use the symbol Δ to represent the total splitting between t_{2g} and e_g orbitals. (Other authors use $10Dq$ or $E_1 - E_2$ to represent this quantity.) We shall choose

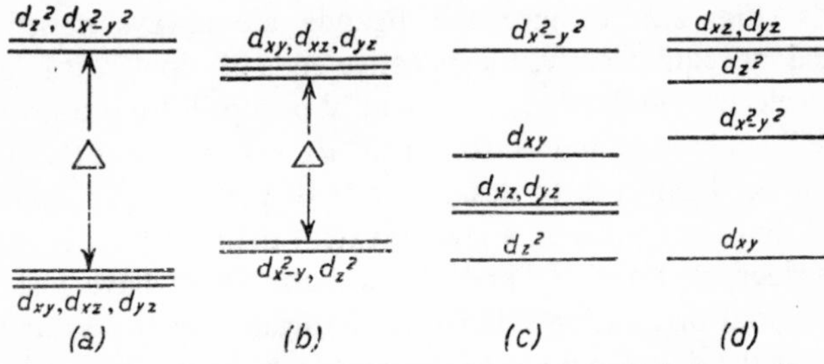

Fig. 2.2.2. Energy level schemes for (a) octahedral coordination, (b) tetrahedral and cubic coordination, (c) square planar coordination, (d) the $[Mo(CN)_8]^{4-}$ *structure*

the energy zero as the *weighted* mean energy of the *d* orbitals, thus making the t_{2g} and e_g energies $-\frac{2}{5}\Delta$ and $\frac{3}{5}\Delta$ respectively. This choice requires some comment.

It might have been thought that the most convenient choice of an energy zero would take account of the absolute energy of the *d* electrons, relative say to a free electron. It turns out, however, that the quantities which can usefully be calculated from the electrostatic crystal-field model all depend on the energy separation between the *d* orbitals of the t_{2g} and e_g groups, and not on their absolute energy. It is then a matter of purely arithmetical convenience to put the mean energy equal to zero, for if some other choice were made it would necessitate the carrying of quantities through energy calculations which finally cancel out. It should not be thought that the lack of dependence of the results of crystal-field calculations on the absolute energy of the *d* orbitals means that this energy is unimportant. On the contrary, it shows that the crystal-field theory is limited in application to those problems which do not depend on absolute energies. Fortunately these problems are of considerable interest.

We next turn to the case of a metal ion in a tetrahedral environment. In Fig. 2.2.3 we compare the position of the d_{xy} and $d_{x^2-y^2}$ orbitals relative to the ligands. It is immediately apparent that each lobe of the d_{xy} orbital comes close to one ligand and that the lobes of the $d_{x^2-y^2}$ orbital lie on the bisectors of the angles between pairs of ligands. Calculations confirm the obvious inference that the $d_{x^2-y^2}$ is repelled less by the ligands than is the d_{xy}

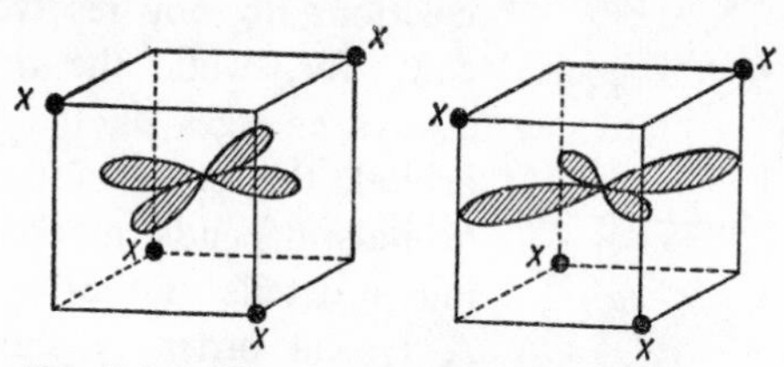

Fig. 2.2.3. The $d_{x^2-y^2}$ and d_{xy} orbitals in a tetrahedral environment

orbital. Symmetry arguments precisely equivalent to those given for the octahedral complexes now show that the d_{xz} and d_{yz} orbitals are degenerate with the d_{xy} orbital and the d_{z^2} orbital with the $d_{x^2-y^2}$ orbital.

We have found again, as with octahedral complexes, that the orbitals split into a group of three orbitals, which we designate as t_2, and a group of two orbitals, which we designate as e. The order of these levels, however, is inverted relative to that for octahedral environments, the t_2 level being *less* stable than the e level. A comparison of Figs. 2.2.1 and 2.2.3 suggests that the splitting is smaller for tetrahedral than for octahedral complexes, and this too is confirmed both by calculation and by experiment. Elementary calculations based on the simplest electrostatic model suggest that the field due to a tetrahedron of negative ions or dipoles is just 4/9 that of an octahedron of these ions or dipoles at an identical distance from the metal.

In no other important case is the splitting of the d orbitals into groups as simple as those which we have so far treated although, for completeness, we mention that the splitting due to a cubic environment of eight ligands is just like that for a tetrahedral environment. The most important environment of lower symmetry commonly encountered in transition-metal chemistry consists of four ligands arranged at the corners of a square with the metal ion at the centre. A glance at Fig. 2.2.1 shows very clearly that in this instance the $d_{x^2-y^2}$ orbital must be less stable than any other orbital. It is not obvious, however, what the order of the remaining orbitals should be, for they all avoid the ligands to some extent, and in ways which make it difficult to guess the relative magnitude of the electron repulsion energies (except that these are identical for the d_{xz} and d_{yz} orbitals). Calculations do not resolve this difficulty for, while the $d_{x^2-y^2}$ orbital always emerges as the least stable orbital, the order of the remaining orbitals depends markedly on the minor details of the model chosen. A typical order is shown in Fig. 2.2.2*c*.

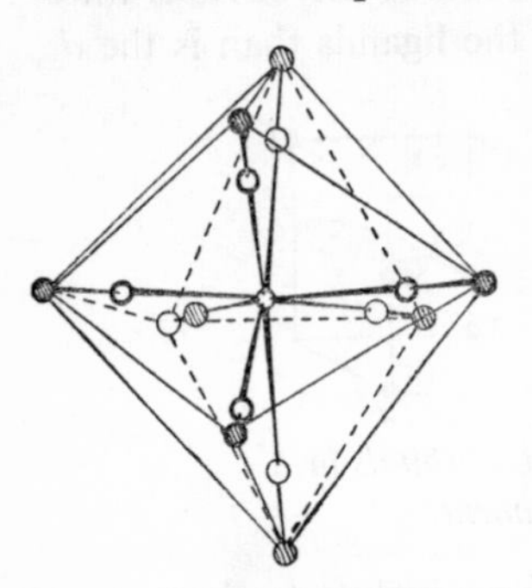

Fig. 2.2.4. The $[Mo(CN)_8]^{4-}$ *arrangement*

In Fig. 2.2.2*d* we show the orbital energy scheme calculated for the curious eight-coordinated structure (Fig. 2.2.4) encountered in the $[Mo(CN)_8]^{4-}$ and $[Re(CN)_8]^{3-}$ ions. We shall return to a discussion of its significance in Section 5.4.

2.3. The molecular-orbital theory[3]

A completely different approach to the problem of orbital energies has been developed in the theory of covalent molecules, particularly for diatomic molecules and aromatic hydrocarbons. In this theory we attempt to find orbitals fulfilling the same function for molecules as the familiar *s*, *p*, *d* orbitals do for atoms. The electronic structure of a molecule is then described, at least for most familiar covalent molecules, by assigning electrons, two at a time, to the orbitals in order of increasing energy. We shall find later that this procedure is not completely satisfactory for transition-metal compounds, but the derivation of the molecular orbitals none the less follows the routine course.

A great simplification of the procedure for determining these orbitals comes about when the molecule concerned has high symmetry. The general group theoretical rule is that only orbitals which transform as the same representation of the molecular point group can combine together to give molecular orbitals.[4] Luckily we can derive all the important results for octahedral complexes without recourse to mathematical arguments.

In so far as it applies to metal complexes the essential content of the group theoretical result is that the symmetry of orbitals on metal and ligand must match. We illustrate this by examples rather than by trying to make it precise by formal definition. Consider a linear molecule XH_2 (Fig. 2.3.1). The 1*s* orbitals on the H atoms, designated ϕ_{1s_A} and ϕ_{1s_B} respectively, can be combined to give new orbitals

$$\psi_1 = \frac{1}{\sqrt{2}}(\phi_{1s_A} + \phi_{1s_B}),$$

$$\psi_2 = \frac{1}{\sqrt{2}}(\phi_{1s_A} - \phi_{1s_B}),$$

which have the important property of being unchanged or changing only in sign when subjected to any of the symmetry operation of the molecule.* ψ_1 is unaffected by reflection in a plane perpendicular to the molecular axis and containing the central atom (the *xy* plane) while ψ_2 changes sign on such a reflection. Our rule about the matching of symmetry properties of molecules shows that ψ_1 can combine with an *s* orbital on the metal atom since the latter is unaffected by reflection in the *xy* plane while ψ_2 can combine with a p_z orbital which changes sign under this operation (Fig. 2.3.1).

Next consider the combination of the p_x orbital on the central atom with the 1*s* orbitals. On reflection in the *yz* plane the p_x orbital changes sign while the orbitals ψ_1 and ψ_2 are unchanged. Hence no combination is possible. Proceeding in this way the reader should convince himself that of the *d* orbitals only the d_{z^2} can combine with ψ_1 and that none can combine with ψ_2.

As a second simple example we take another hypothetical case,

* In forming complete molecular orbitals from metal and ligand orbitals the latter should always be combined to give such symmetry orbitals as a first step.

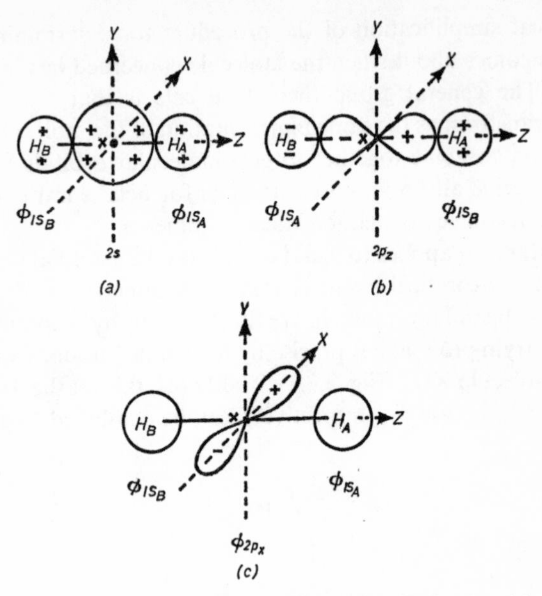

Fig. 2.3.1. Orbitals for an XH_2 *molecule showing (a) and (b) bonding orbitals, (c) the inability of the* p_x *orbital to combine with s orbitals*

that of a planar XH_4 molecule. We consider only the d orbitals of the central ion and we choose the bond directions as the x and y axes. We now notice the d_{xz} and d_{yz} orbitals change sign on reflection in the molecular plane (Fig. 2.1.1*b*) and so cannot combine with s orbitals. Furthermore the d_{xy} orbital changes sign on reflection either in the x or y axis, and no combination of s orbitals can do this (although the combination $\phi_{s_1} + \phi_{s_2}$ changes sign on reflection in the y axis only).

The orbital $d_{x^2-y^2}$ can combine with the linear combination of hydrogen orbitals $\frac{1}{2}(\phi_1 + \phi_2 - \phi_3 - \phi_4)$ as may be seen by confirming that these two orbitals are affected in the same way by all the symmetry operations of the molecule. Similarly the d_{z^2} orbital can combine with the combination $\frac{1}{2}(\phi_1 + \phi_2 + \phi_3 + \phi_4)$ since both are unaffected by all the symmetry operations of the molecule (Fig. 2.3.2).

We now consider the case of an octahedral complex and suppose at first that the metal ion has available for bond formation,

TABLE 2.3.1

Symmetry classification of orbitals for octahedral complexes

For numbering of ligands see Fig. 2.5.1. (T_{1g} and T_{2u} orbitals neglected)

	Metal orbital	Ligand σ	Ligand π
A_{1g}	$4s$	$\chi_{a_1} = \frac{1}{\sqrt{6}}(\phi_1 + \phi_2 + \phi_3 + \phi_4 + \phi_5 + \phi_6)$	
E_g	$3d_{z^2}$	$\chi_{e_g, z^2} = \frac{1}{2\sqrt{3}}(2\phi_5 + 2\phi_6 - \phi_1 - \phi_2 - \phi_3 - \phi_4)$	
	$3d_{x^2-y^2}$	$\chi_{e_g, x^2-y^2} = \frac{1}{2}(\phi_1 + \phi_2 - \phi_3 - \phi_4)$	
T_{1u}	$4p_x$	$\chi_{t_{1u}, x} = \frac{1}{\sqrt{2}}(\phi_1 - \phi_2)$	$\pi t_{1u, x} = \frac{1}{2}(\pi_{3x} + \pi_{4x} + \pi_{5x} + \pi_{6x})$
	$4p_y$	$\chi_{t_{1u}, y} = \frac{1}{\sqrt{2}}(\phi_3 - \phi_4)$	$\pi t_{1u, y} = \frac{1}{2}(\pi_{1y} + \pi_{2y} + \pi_{5y} + \pi_{6y})$
	$4p_z$	$\chi_{t_{1u},} = \frac{1}{\sqrt{2}}(\phi_5 - \phi_6)$	$\pi t_{1u, z} = \frac{1}{2}(\pi_{1z} + \pi_{2z} + \pi_{3z} + \pi_{4z})$
T_{2g}	$3d_{xy}$		$\pi t_{2g, xy} = \frac{1}{2}(\pi_{1y} - \pi_{2y} + \pi_{3y} - \pi_{4y})$
	$3d_{xz}$		$\pi t_{2g, xz} = \frac{1}{2}(\pi_{1z} - \pi_{2z} + \pi_{5x} - \pi_{6x})$
	$3d_{yz}$		$\pi t_{2g, yz} = \frac{1}{2}(\pi_{3z} - \pi_{4z} + \pi_{5y} - \pi_{6y})$

ns, *np* and $(n-1)$ *d* orbitals, e.g. 4*s*, 4*p* and 3*d* orbitals in the first transition series. In column 1 of Table 2.3.1 we note the group theoretical classification of orbitals, which we here regard merely as convenient abbreviations for the orbitals appearing in column 2 of the table. In column 3 we show the linear combinations of σ orbitals* on the ligands which can combine with the metal orbitals. The resultant (bonding) molecular orbitals are illustrated in Fig. 2.3.3.

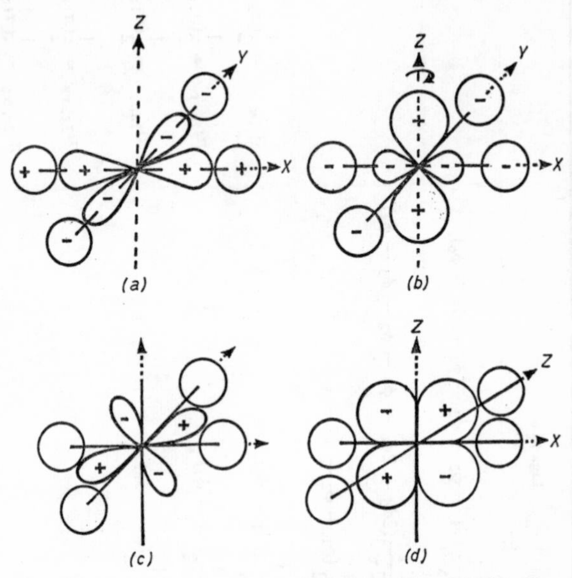

Fig. 2.3.2. Orbitals for an XY_4 *complex (a) bonding* $d_{x^2-y^2}$ *combinations, (b) the weakly bonding* d_{z^2} *combination, (c) and (d) orbital which cannot form* σ *bonds*

We now return to an important rule of elementary molecular-orbital theory. Whenever two orbitals combine to form more extensively delocalized molecular orbitals two new orbitals are obtained, one of which is more stable and the other less stable than either of the original orbitals. More generally the number of new orbitals formed is equal to the number of combining orbitals,

* σ orbitals are *s* orbitals or *p* orbitals pointing along the bond directions or more generally any orbitals having roughly axial symmetry about the bond directions.

and one of the new orbitals is less and another more stable than any of the combining orbitals. (In this more general case we cannot say anything further about the relative energies of the orbitals. Only detailed calculation can show whether an orbital of intermediate energy is raised or lowered by the interaction.)

In the light of these considerations we can draw the energy-level diagram shown in Fig. 2.3.4. This diagram is not based on

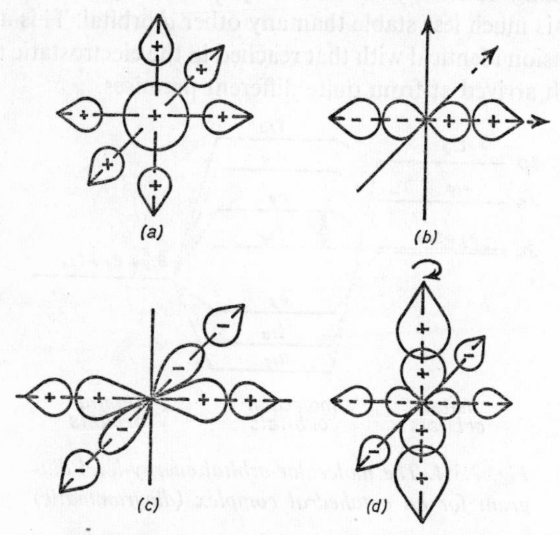

Fig. 2.3.3. The σ bonding orbitals of an octahedral complex involving (a) the s, (b) the p_x, (p_y and p_z) orbitals, (c) the $3d_{x^2-y^2}$ orbital, (d) the $3d_{z^2}$ orbital

fundamental calculation but is to be regarded as at best semi-empirical. It is consistent with the elementary molecular-orbital theory arguments and gives agreement with experiment. The order of the bonding a_{1g}, t_{1u} and e_g orbitals is unknown, but fortunately irrelevant for our purposes. Similarly the order of the a_{1g} and t_{1u} antibonding orbitals is undecided and very probably varies from compound to compound. The key result, as we shall see, is that the t_{2g} *d* orbitals are unaffected by σ bonding while the e_g orbitals combine with ligand orbitals to give a doubly-degenerate bonding orbital and a doubly-degenerate antibonding orbital. Provided the ligand orbitals are more stable than the metal orbitals the bonding orbital is mainly a ligand orbital and the antibonding orbital mainly a metal orbital.*

An exactly similar argument may be applied to a square planar complex. It has already been noted that of the *d* orbitals only the $d_{x^2-y^2}$ and the d_{z^2} orbital can form σ bonds with the ligands. Detailed calculations show that the $d_{x^2-y^2}$ orbital is much more affected by such bonding than the d_{z^2} orbital and hence that the antibonding combination of the $d_{x^2-y^2}$ orbital with the ligand orbitals is much less stable than any other *d* orbital. This again is a conclusion identical with that reached in the electrostatic theory, although arrived at from quite different premises.

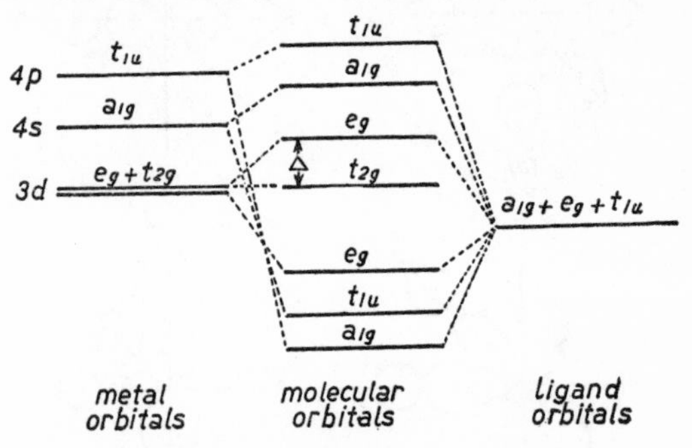

Fig. 2.3.4. The molecular-orbital energy-level diagram for an octahedral complex (diagrammatic)

Application of this theory to tetrahedral complexes is more complicated, although similar in principle. We shall not give further details except to say that the t_2 *d* orbitals, almost certainly extensively mixed with the *p* orbitals, can take part in the formation of σ bonds, while the *e* orbitals cannot. It seems very probable that detailed calculations would show that the t_2 *d* orbitals are fairly strongly antibonding, but this conclusion is not immediate and hence the argument is less clear-cut than for octahedral or planar complexes.

It is often convenient to know which orbitals can be used to form bonds in complexes of any prescribed symmetry.[5] For this purpose we have gathered together a number of results in Table 2.3.2. From the table one can see which metal orbitals can be used

* This follows from the theory which shows that a molecular orbital formed from two component orbitals includes a larger contribution from that component which is closer in energy.

in σ bonding and which in π bonding (see Section 2.5) for most of the arrangements of ligands which have been observed.

TABLE 2.3.2

Bonding orbitals for molecules of high symmetry

The z axis is chosen as the molecular axis of highest symmetry for 2-, 3- and 5-fold coordination. The choice of axes for the tetrahedron, octahedron and cube is that used in the text. Structures of lower symmetry are not included since the present technique is not very useful for them.

Coordination number	Stereochemistry	Orbitals for σ bonds	Orbitals for π bonds
2	Linear	s, p_z d_{z^2}, p_z	p_x, p_y d_{xz}, d_{yz}
3	Planar Equilateral triangle	s, p_x, p_y d_{z^2}, p_x, p_y	p_z d_{xz}, d_{yz}
4	Square Planar	$d_{x^2-y^2}, s, p_x, p_y$ $d_{x^2-y^2}, d_{z^2}, p_x, p_y$	p_z d_{xz}, d_{yz}
	Tetrahedral	s, p_x, p_y, p_z $s, d_{xy}, d_{xz}, d_{yz}$	p_x, p_y, p_z $d_{xy}, d_{xz}, d_{yz}; d_{x^2-y^2}, d_{z^2}$
5	Trigonal Bipyramid	$s, p_x, p_y, p_z, d_{z^2}$	p_x, p_y, p_z $d_{xz}, d_{yz}; d_{x^2-y^2}, d_{xy}$
6	Octahedron	$s, p_x, p_y, p_z,$ $d_{x^2-y^2}, d_{z^2}$	$p_x, p_y, p_z,$ d_{xy}, d_{xz}, d_{yz}
8	Cube	$s, p_x, p_y, p_z, d_{xy}, d_{xz},$ d_{yz}, f_{xyz}	p_x, p_y, p_z $d_{xy}, d_{xz}, d_{yz}, d_{x^2-y^2},$ d_{z^2}

2.4. Ions with a single *d* electron – the $[Ti(H_2O)_6]^{3+}$ ion

We consider the ion $[Ti(H_2O)_6]^{3+}$ as a simple example, first from the point of view of the electrostatic theory and then from that of the molecular-orbital theory. In the electrostatic theory we have a single *d* electron which must be accommodated in the t_{2g} or e_g orbital. Clearly in the ground state it goes into the lowest orbital, the t_{2g} orbital, so the ion is described as having a closed shell core outside of which a single d electron is present in a triply degenerate t_{2g} orbital.

What predictions can we make? The simplest is that there should be an electronic transition in which the solitary d electron is transferred from the t_{2g} to the less stable e_g orbital and that this should occur at a frequency corresponding to the separation Δ between the two types of orbital. In fact, there is a single absorption band in the visible spectrum of $[Ti(H_2O)_6]^{3+}$ occurring at 5,000 Å [6] (Fig. 2.4.1). While this band cannot be identified as the $t_{2g} \rightarrow e_g$ electronic transition without further checks, there is now ample

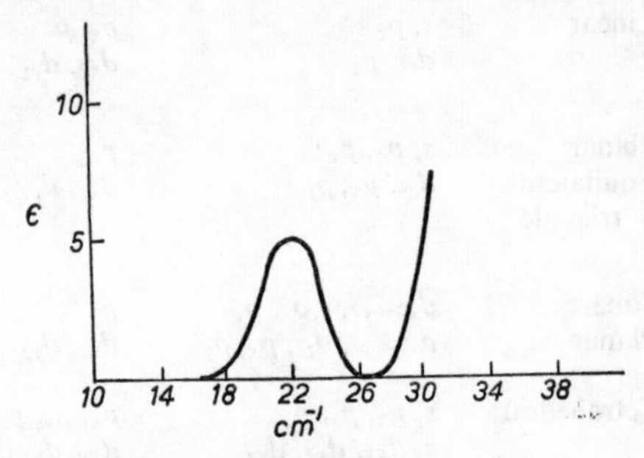

Fig. 2.4.1. The spectrum of the $[Ti(H_2O)_6]^{3+}$ ion

confirmatory evidence for the identification. This observation gives us our first empirical evidence about the size of Δ, namely, that it is 20,000 cm.$^{-1}$ or about 60 Kcals.* in $[Ti(H_2O)_6]^{3+}$.

We now turn to the molecular-orbital description of this same ion. We consider only the two electrons in the σ unshared pair orbital on each water molecule and the d electron on the Ti^{3+} ion. We should, in a complete treatment, discuss all of the other electrons of the water molecule, but at the present stage this would so complicate the picture as to obscure the most interesting qualitative features of the problem. Later we shall occasionally have to consider electrons other than the σ unshared-pair electrons of the ligands, but even then we shall be highly selective.

* We shall give energies in cm.$^{-1}$, Kcals. or electron volts, whichever is convenient. The conversion factors are:

$$1 \text{ e.v.} = 8{,}068 \text{ cm.}^{-1} = 23{\cdot}063 \text{ Kcals.}$$

In all, then, there are thirteen electrons to be accommodated in the molecular orbitals of Fig. 2.3.4. Clearly the first twelve fill the bonding a_{1g}, e_g and t_{1u} orbitals forming six bonds. This leaves over one electron to go into the t_{2g} orbital. Just as before, we expect a single low-energy electronic transition, essentially within the *d* shell, between a t_{2g} orbital and an e_g orbital, and this we identify with the observed band at 5,000 Å.

This description differs from that given by the electrostatic theory only in that we now say that the electron is transferred from the non-bonding t_{2g} orbital to the antibonding e_g orbital. The symmetry and basic composition of the orbitals assumed to be involved in the transition are unchanged, but we attribute the instability of the e_g orbital relative to the t_{2g} orbital to the anti-bonding character of the former, rather than to its less favourable electrostatic interaction with the ligands.

2.5. The effect of double-bonding[7]

The idea of double-bonding is, of course, foreign to the electrostatic approach to transition-metal chemistry. In the molecular-orbital theory it leads to a natural extension of the theory of σ bonding.

We consider an octahedral complex as in Section 2.3, but now we include in our treatment a pair of orbitals of π symmetry on each of the six ligands. We number the atoms as shown in Fig. 2.5.1 and designate as π_{iz} an orbital on the *i*'th atom which has the *xy* plane as a nodal plane, etc. If the π orbitals are *p* orbitals, then π_{iz} is just p_{iz} and the reason for this choice of notation is obvious. More generally, however, π_{iz} may be, for example, a d_{xz} orbital.

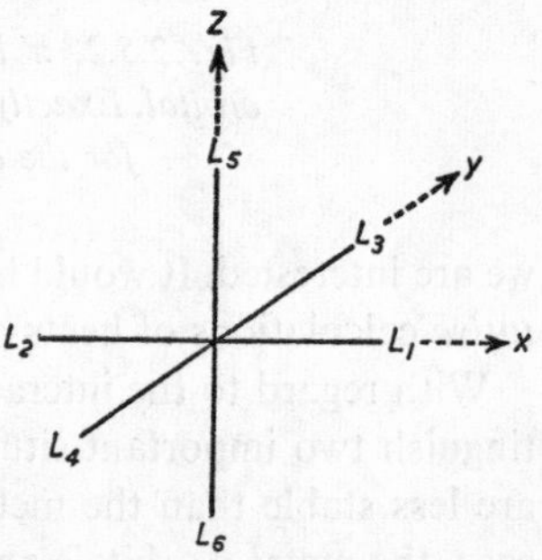

Fig. 2.5.1. Numbering of ligands in an octahedral complex

In column four of Table 2.3.1 we have noted the correct linear combinations of the twelve ligand π orbitals corresponding to the symmetry of an octahedral complex. It should be noted that two (t_{1g} and t_{2u}) of the four triply degenerate π molecular orbitals do not combine with any metal *s*, *p* or *d* orbitals and have been omitted from the table. The t_{2g} π molecular orbitals combine with the previously non-bonding t_{2g} *d* orbitals as shown for the d_{xy} orbital in Fig. 2.5.2. Also, the t_{1u} molecular orbital has the right symmetry to combine with the *p* orbitals of the metal, although the latter are already involved in σ bonding. We neglect the latter combination, because it is not easy to discuss qualitatively and because it has little influence on the properties of transition-metal ions in which

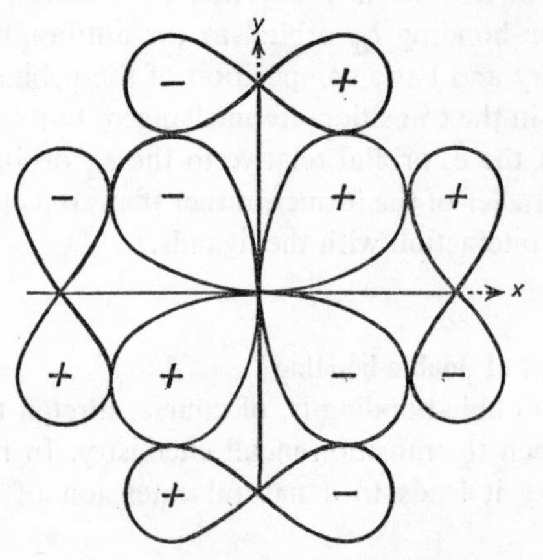

Fig. 2.5.2. π bonding involving the d_{xy} orbital. Exactly similar bonding is possible for the d_{xz} and d_{yz} orbitals

we are interested. It would have to be taken into account in *quantitative* calculations of heats of formation, lattice energies, etc.

With regard to the interaction of the t_{2g} *d* orbitals we may distinguish two important situations. In the first the ligand orbitals are less stable than the metal *d* orbitals and unoccupied. In this case, the metal *d* orbitals are stabilized by the interaction and the separation Δ between t_{2g} and e_g orbitals is thus increased (Fig. 2.5.3*a*). In the second case, the ligand *d* orbitals are stable and occupied. Then the t_{2g} *d* orbitals are antibonding and are raised in energy by the interaction (Fig. 2.5.3*b*). This leads to a decrease in Δ.

Ligands which have empty π orbitals, and hence form compounds having Δ values increased by double-bonding, include

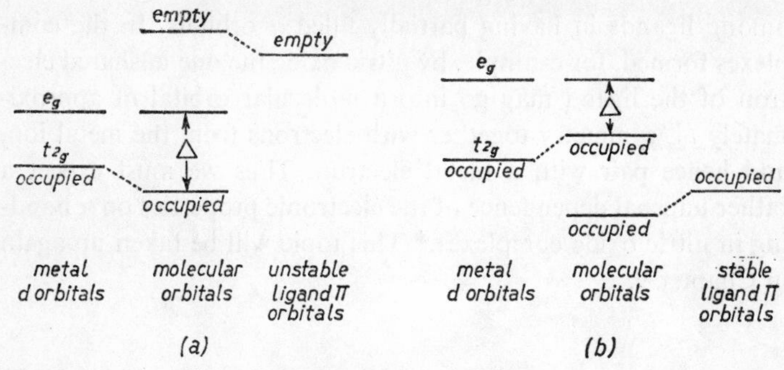

Fig. 2.5.3. The effect of π bonding on Δ, (a) for acceptor ligand orbitals, (b) for donor ligand orbitals

particularly the phosphines, arsines, etc., for in these, although the *d* orbitals are not stable enough to become occupied, they are stable enough to take part in bonding.[7] Ligands in which the π orbitals are filled include, for example, the fluoride and oxide ions; the water molecule has one occupied π orbital. In all cases, double-bonding leads to decreased Δ values in complexes of these ligands.

There are a large number of molecules which have both filled (donor) and empty (acceptor) π orbitals; for example, the cyanide ion has both filled and empty π molecular orbitals, while the chloride ion has occupied $3p_\pi$ and empty $3d_\pi$ orbitals. Usually it is possible to say whether donor or acceptor interaction will predominate; the acceptor action is most important for CO and usually for the cyanide ion; the donor p_π action in the case of the Cl^- ion is usually stronger than the acceptor d_π action, etc. However, one must be cautious in applying such conclusions, for it may happen that an ion which is a π donor in complexes of moderate valency becomes an effective π acceptor if the metal ion is in a sufficiently low valency. Conversely, an ion which is an acceptor in low-valency complexes may become a donor when complexed with a high-valency metal ion. Thus in the $[Mo(CN)_8]^{3-}$ the CN^- ions may well act as donors rather than as acceptors, while in zero-valent complexes halogens may act as acceptors.*

Finally, we note that nitric oxide, and oxygen, are exceptional

* But see the discussion of simultaneous donor and acceptor action in Chapter 9.

among ligands in having partially filled π orbitals. In the complexes formed, for example, by nitric oxide the one unshared electron of the ligand may go into a molecular orbital of approximately t_{2g} symmetry together with electrons from the metal ion, and hence pair with a metal electron. Thus we must expect a rather unusual dependence of the electronic properties on π bonding in nitric oxide complexes.* This topic will be taken up again in Chapter 9.

2.6. A provisional attitude to the bonding in transition-metal complexes

We have found in a number of examples that the principal features of the orbital energy-level diagram for *d* electrons turn out to be the same in both the electrostatic and the molecular-orbital theories. Later we shall see that these energy-level diagrams may be used to systematize a good deal of transition-metal chemistry. Should we attempt to choose between the rival theories?

The evidence that has accumulated in the past decade or so has made it quite clear that if either approach is adopted to the exclusion of the other there is no hope of providing a unified theory of even the better understood parts of transition-metal chemistry and physics. For this reason it has been proposed that to a crude first approximation we discuss many problems in terms of the energy-level diagrams without worrying at first about the origins of the energy differences between the various *d* orbitals. Later we shall find it of interest to investigate or speculate about, for example, the relative importance of σ bonding, π bonding and electrostatic effects in one or another class of compound; we may even decide to consider quite new effects to account for part of the *d* orbital energy differences. The results of further work of this kind may be expected to amplify our qualitative conclusions, but it should not affect their validity in so far as they are independent of the mechanism of *d* orbital splitting.

The term 'Ligand-Field Theory' has been suggested and quite

* Usually there are no π electrons on the ligands or just enough to fill the stable orbitals. Then the ligand electrons turn out to be present in just sufficient numbers to *fill* molecular orbitals of the complex, so that no interference with the number of unpaired electrons of the metal ion is possible.

widely accepted to cover a more general hybrid approach to transition-metal chemistry, which is consistent with this point of view. In it, we suppose that ligand-field splittings, for example in octahedral complexes, are the result of a number of more or less independent and complementary mechanisms. The total splitting is thought of as the algebraic sum of a number of individual contributions, due to electrostatic effects, σ bonding, π bonding, etc. Even this, however, is not a completely satisfactory position and one must look forward to a more complete theory, perhaps a molecular-orbital theory, in which all important electrostatic interactions are dealt with in detail. Such a theory would contain the electrostatic and elementary molecular-orbital theories as important, but never realized, limiting cases.

At this point we may say something about the direct calculation of ligand-field splittings. Calculations based on a point charge or point dipole model for the ligands are quite straightforward provided the *d* electron radial wave-function is known. Generally they lead to crystal splittings smaller than those found experimentally. Agreement with experiment can be achieved by postulating a suitable amount of polarization of the ligands by the central ion, but the legitimacy of such procedures is difficult to assess. In general, I feel that the electrostatic theories give the correct order of magnitude for the splittings, but do not give satisfactory quantitative agreement with experiment.

Clearly there are many possible explanations of this. Agreement might be improved by using a more realistic charge distribution to represent the ligands than the usual point charge model. Mainly, however, I suspect that the difficulty is that of taking account of covalent bonding and polarization, which are closely related, but not identical, phenomena.

CHAPTER TWO

REVIEW REFERENCES, ETC.

2.1

HARTREE, *The Calculation of Atomic Structures.* Wiley, New York, 1957

PAULING and WILSON, *Introduction to Quantum Mechanics.* McGraw-Hill, New York, 1935

2.2

GRIFFITH and ORGEL, *Quart. Rev.*, **XI,** 381 (1957)

HARTMANN, *Theorie der Chemische Bindung und Quantum-Theoretische Grundlage*. Springer Verlag, 1956

LINNETT, *Faraday Society Discussion*, **No. 26,** 7 (1958)

MOFFITT and BALLHAUSEN, *Ann. Rev. of Phys. Chem.*, **7,** 107 (1956)

NYHOLM, *Report of the 10th Solvay Conference in Chemistry, Brussels, 1956*, p. 225

ORGEL, *Report of the 10th Solvay Conference in Chemistry, Brussels, 1956*, p. 289

2.3

COULSON, *Quart. Revs.*, **1,** 144 (1947)

COULSON, *Valence*. Oxford University Press, 1952

1. BETHE, *Ann. Physik* (5), **3,** 133 (1929)
2. VAN VLECK, *The Theory of Electric and Magnetic Susceptibilities*. Oxford University Press, 1932, Chapter II
3. VAN VLECK, *J. Chem. Phys.*, **3,** 803 and 807 (1935)
4. EYRING, WALTER and KIMBALL, *Quantum Chemistry*. Wiley, New York, 1944, Chapter X
5. KIMBALL, *J. Chem. Phys.*, **8,** 188 (1940)
6. HARTMANN and SCHLÄFER, *Z. physik. Chem.*, **197,** 116 (1951)
7. CRAIG, MACCOLL, NYHOLM, ORGEL and SUTTON, *J. Chem. Soc.*, 332 (1954)

CHAPTER THREE

Ions with several *d* Electrons

3.1. The distribution of electrons between the t_{2g} and e_g orbitals

The electronic properties of free transition-metal atoms and ions are determined partly by the interactions of the *d* electrons with the nucleus and electronic core and partly by the interaction between different *d* electrons. We shall for the most part be concerned with the second of these interactions for the first changes little when a metal ion becomes part of a crystal or complex and so has little influence on the bonding.

There are two sources of interaction between the *d* electrons, both ultimately due to their mutual electrostatic repulsion. The first can be understood classically; it is just equal to the repulsion between two *classical* charge densities having the same spatial distribution as that given by interpreting ϕ^2, the square of the wave-function for an electron, as an electron density. Clearly it leads to the stabilization of states of polyelectronic atoms in which the electrons are on the average far apart relative to those in which the electrons are close together.

The second and more important interaction is the so-called exchange interaction. It has no classical analogue, for its magnitude depends on the arrangement of the spins of the different electrons. In general the exchange interaction leads to a stabilization of an atom which increases with the number of unpaired electrons having parallel spins. It is the nature of this dependence on the number of parallel electron spins which is the basis of Hund's rules for determining the ground states of polyelectronic atoms.

Consider an ion with *n d* electrons and all other electrons paired off in filled shells. If $n \leqslant 5$ the exchange interaction guarantees that in the ground state all electrons must have parallel spins. When there is more than one state satisfying this spin condition the nature of the ground state depends on the details of the classical electrostatic repulsion and exchange interactions for the different possible states. The ground states, using standard spectroscopic notation,* are ^2D, ^3F, ^4F, ^5D and ^6S for $n = 1, 2, 3, 4$ and 5 respectively.

If there are more than five d electrons present spin-pairing must of necessity occur. The ground states still have the maximum number of unpaired electrons consistent with the requirements of the Pauli principle.† They are ^5D, ^4F, ^3F, ^2D and ^1S for d^6, d^7, d^8, d^9 and d^{10} configurations, respectively.

The special stability of half-filled and filled d electron shells is closely connected with the exchange energy. When a fifth electron is added to a d^4 ion it has its spin parallel to the four spins already on the metal. Hence it is strongly stabilized by the exchange energy. On the other hand a sixth electron must have its spin antiparallel to *all* of the electrons already present and so is not stabilized at all. It follows that a d^5 ion resists both addition and removal of d electrons rather strongly. This is what is meant by the 'stability of the half-filled shell', which must not be taken to imply anything about the strength of metal–ligand interactions. In fact these latter are particularly weak for high-spin d^5 complexes. Analogous arguments apply to d^{10} ions.

Now suppose that a transition-metal ion is introduced into an octahedral environment. The d orbitals split up into the lower t_{2g} and the upper e_g orbitals in the manner discussed in the last chapter. Just as in other molecules there will now be a tendency for the available electrons to fill first the lowest orbitals, that is, for the d electrons to fill the t_{2g} orbitals before beginning to go into the upper e_g orbitals.

If there are two or three electrons present these can go into the t_{2g} orbital with their spins parallel. In this way the demand for a maximum exchange energy and the requirement that the lowest orbitals are filled before the upper ones may be satisfied simultaneously. If there are eight, nine, or ten d electrons present then by placing six electrons in the t_{2g} orbital and two, three or four,

* For the present it is sufficient to recall that the superscript which appears in these symbols is equal to $n + 1$ where n is equal to the number of unpaired electrons.

† The Pauli principle requires that no two electrons with the same spin can occupy the same orbital.

respectively, in the e_g orbital, we can again satisfy the requirements for optimum exchange and for optimum orbital energies. (See Table 3.1.1.)

If there are present four, five, six or seven d electrons then a new and interesting situation arises. Either we may maintain the maximum number of unpaired spins, that is, the number in the free ion, or we may place a maximum number of electrons in the t_{2g} orbital, but we cannot do both. Effectively then we find a competition between the exchange forces which tend to keep the free ion arrangement with a maximum number of parallel spins and the ligand-field which tends to force electrons into the t_{2g} orbital, even though this can only be done by pairing spins. This is illustrated in Table 3.1.1.

TABLE 3.1.1

d electrons in octahedral complexes

n = number of unpaired spins; μ = predicted spin-only moment in Bohr magnetons

Number of d electrons	Arrangement in weak ligand-field		n	μ	Arrangement in strong ligand-field		n	μ
	t	e			t	e		
1	↑	—	1	1·73	↑	—	1	1·73
2	↑ ↑	—	2	2·83	↑ ↑	—	2	2·83
3	↑ ↑ ↑	—	3	3·87	↑ ↑ ↑	—	3	3·87
4	↑ ↑ ↑	↑	4	4·90	↑↓ ↑ ↑	—	2	2·83
5	↑ ↑ ↑	↑ ↑	5	5·92	↑↓ ↑↓ ↑	—	1	1·73
6	↑↓ ↑ ↑	↑ ↑	4	4·90	↑↓ ↑↓ ↑↓	—	0	0
7	↑↓ ↑↓ ↑	↑ ↑	3	3·87	↑↓ ↑↓ ↑↓	↑	1	1·73
8	↑↓ ↑↓ ↑↓	↑ ↑	2	2·83	↑↓ ↑↓ ↑↓	↑ ↑	2	2·83
9	↑↓ ↑↓ ↑↓	↑↓ ↑	1	1·73	↑↓ ↑↓ ↑↓	↑↓ ↑	1	1·73

Naturally in a situation such as this it is a quantitative matter to determine which effect dominates. We may, however, be quite sure that if the ligand-field is *big enough* it must overcome the exchange forces and the spin-paired or low-spin complex will then be stable. For this reason complexes with the lower number of unpaired electrons are often known as high-field complexes, and the conditions in which they occur as high-field conditions. In a similar way we are sure that for sufficiently low ligand-fields the exchange forces must prevail, for the free atom or ion may be thought to correspond to the limit of the process in which the ligand-field is gradually reduced to zero. Compounds of transition-metal ions having a maximum number of unpaired electrons are therefore known as low-field compounds.

Molecules with unpaired electrons are generally paramagnetic, and to a first approximation the paramagnetic contribution to the susceptibility is proportional to $4S(S+1) = n(n+2)$ where $S = \frac{1}{2}n$ is the resultant spin due to n unpaired electrons. (See Appendix.) It follows that magnetic susceptibility measurements distinguish between high-spin and low-spin complexes. The anticipated magnetic moments derived from the above simple expression are included in Table 3.1.1.

The reader familiar with Pauling's 'Magnetic Criterion for Bond Type' will remember that the empirical criteria used by Pauling to distinguish between ionic and covalent bonds are just the ones which we regard as distinguishing high-field from low-field compounds. In later sections we shall discuss the relation between the ligand-field strength and the degree of covalency of the bonds formed by the metal ion to see whether it justifies the use of Pauling's criterion.

In octahedral complexes with 5 or 6 d electrons there is in addition to the high-spin and low-spin configurations an intermediate configuration which has three unpaired spins for d^5 ions and two for d^6 ions. It is a consequence of the detailed theory of spin-pairing that ions with these intermediate configurations are not expected to occur in regular octahedral environments.[1] They may, however, exist in planar or in octahedral but irregular environments and paramagnetic resonance studies make it very probable that certain phthalocyanine complexes of the Fe^{3+} ion do have three unpaired spins.[2]

3.2. The magnitude of Δ

In this section we shall deviate from a systematic approach to ligand-field theory and make use of some results which will only be discussed in detail in later chapters. The investigation of the electronic absorption spectra of metal ions in their octahedrally coordinated compounds makes it possible to deduce the size of Δ for almost any metal ion and set of ligands. (We have seen how this is done for an ion with only one *d* electron, but a good deal more theory is needed to consider the general case.)

From these interpretations of optical spectra a number of generalizations become apparent:

(1) The complexes of a given ligand with ions of the same row of the periodic table in the same valency have Δ values in a fairly narrow range. Thus Δ for the hydrates of divalent ions of the first series varies from 7,800 $cm.^{-1}$ for the Mn^{2+} ion to about 11,000 $cm.^{-1}$ for the Cr^{2+} ion.

In general the high-spin complexes with five *d* electrons have smaller ligand-fields than do the neighbouring elements in the periodic table. This is connected with the variation of the ionic radii along the transition-metal series.

(2) For the complexes of a given ligand Δ increases rather rapidly with the valency of the metal ion. Thus while the hydrates of divalent ions have $\Delta \approx 10{,}000$ $cm.^{-1}$, the Δ values for trivalent ions of the first series cluster about 20,000 $cm.^{-1}$.

Such generalizations must not be applied too widely. The present one is applicable to 'normal' valencies, say two, three and four. In ions of very low valency double-bonding could possibly become dominant and the crystal-field might rise again with decreasing valency, e.g. with the phenanthroline complexes of zero- and −1-valent metals.

(3) In the corresponding complexes of metals of different transition series Δ increases, often by about 30 per cent, from the first transition series to the second, and by a similar amount from the second to the third series.

(4) The common ligands can be arranged in an order of increasing ligand-field strength such that Δ increases along the series in a manner more or less independent of the particular metal ion studied. Thus the relative size of Δ is a characteristic of a ligand.

Again this generalization must be used cautiously. Firstly, there are a very few minor exceptions even among complexes of divalent and trivalent ions in which complexes of ligands close together in the series have Δ values in the wrong order. More seriously, it is likely that drastic changes of order will occur if compounds of unusual valency are studied. Thus ammonia and phenanthroline have quite similar Δ's in their familiar high-spin complexes. In phenanthroline complexes of zero-valent ions double-bonding must be very important so we may expect Δ to be much larger than for corresponding complexes of non-conjugated amines, if indeed the latter can be made to form at all.

For the common ligands in complexes with metal ions in their normal valencies the order of increasing Δ is found empirically to be:

I^-, Br^-, Cl^-, F^-, C_2H_5OH, H_2O, NH_3,

Ethylenediamine, NO_2^-, CN^-.

TABLE 3.2.1

Values of ligand-field splitting Δ

Values for d^4 and d^9 systems are only approximate
(Italics indicate low-spin complex)
(After C. K. Jørgensen thesis, Copenhagen, 1957)

		6 Br^-	6 Cl^-	6 H_2O	6 NH_3	3 en	6 CN^-
3 d^1	Titanium (III)	—	—	20,300	—	—	—
3 d^2	Vanadium (III)	—	—	17,700	—	—	—
3 d^3	Vanadium (II)	—	—	12,600	—	—	—
	Chromium (III)	—	13,600	17,400	21,600	21,900	26,300
4 d^3	Molybdenum (III)	—	19,200	—	—	—	—
3 d^4	Chromium (II)	—	—	13,900	—	—	—
	Manganese (III)	—	—	21,000	—	—	—
3 d^5	Manganese (II)	—	—	7,800	—	9,100	—
	Iron (III)	—	—	13,700	—	—	—
3 d^6	Iron (II)	—	—	10,400	—	—	*33,000*
	Cobalt (III)	—	—	*18,600*	*23,000*	*23,300*	*34,000*
4 d^6	Rhodium (III)	*18,900*	*20,300*	*27,000*	*33,900*	*34,400*	—
5 d^6	Iridium (III)	*23,100*	*24,900*	—	—	*41,200*	—
	Platinum (IV)	*24,000*	*29,000*	—	—	—	—
3 d^7	Cobalt (II)	—	—	9,300	10,100	11,000	—
3 d^8	Nickel (II)	7,000	7,300	8,500	10,800	11,600	—
3 d^9	Copper (II)	—	—	12,600	15,100	16,400	—

Δ values for other ligands, usually in a less complete range of complexes, are also to be found in the literature. In Table 3.2.1 we give quantitative data determined spectroscopically for many of the most carefully studied ligands.

It will be noticed that while the order of increasing Δ follows one's intuitive ideas about the degree of covalency of the bonds formed by the ligands in the latter part of the series, this is not at all the case among the halides. The ligand-field increases steadily from iodide to fluoride, while the covalency is generally thought to decrease along this series.

3.3. The ease of spin-pairing in octahedral complexes

In this section we consider why it is that certain transition-metal ions form low-spin complexes more readily than others. We adopt a very much over-simplified treatment which illustrates semi-quantitatively the factors involved and agrees at least qualitatively with the results of more detailed quantitative calculations.

Consider first the orbital energies of the weak-field and strong-field complexes with n d electrons. As we have seen, the two energies are equal for up to 3 electrons but different for 4–7 electrons. In general, the strong-field configuration has orbital energy $-\frac{2n}{5}\Delta$ for $n \leqslant 6$ and $-\frac{12}{5}\Delta + \frac{3(n-6)}{5}\Delta$ for $n > 6$. The weak-field energies are somewhat more difficult to write down generally; they are $-\frac{2}{5}\Delta$, $-\frac{4}{5}\Delta$ (approximately), $-\frac{6}{5}\Delta$, $-\frac{3}{5}\Delta$, 0 for $n = 1$ or 6, 2 or 7, 3 or 8, 4 or 9 and 5 or 10, respectively.

We next consider the exchange energy for the various configurations. Instead of making detailed calculations we suppose, as is roughly the case, that an equal exchange stabilization energy is contributed by every distinct pair of electrons with parallel spins. We neglect the classical repulsion energy between electrons since this is usually not so different in the spin-paired and spin-free states. The d^7 complexes cannot be discussed in this simple way; the full treatment shows that they spin-pair less easily than d^6 complexes but more easily than d^5 complexes.[1] The situation is

TABLE 3.3.1

Orbital and exchange energies of *d* electron configurations in octahedral complexes

N = number of distinct pairs of electrons with parallel spins; exchange energy is approximately NK

Number of d electrons	Arrangement in weak ligand-field		N	Arrangement in strong ligand-field		N	Gain in orbital energy in strong field
	t_{2g}	e_g		t_{2g}	e_g		
1	↑	—	0	↑	—	0	0
2	↑ ↑	—	1	↑ ↑	—	1	0
3	↑ ↑ ↑	—	3	↑ ↑ ↑	—	3	0
4	↑ ↑ ↑	↑	6	↑↓ ↑ ↑	—	3	Δ
5	↑ ↑ ↑	↑ ↑	10	↑↓ ↑↓ ↑	—	4	2Δ
6	↑↓ ↑ ↑	↑ ↑	10	↑↓ ↑↓ ↑↓	—	6	2Δ
7	↑↓ ↑↓ ↑	↑ ↑	11	↑↓ ↑↓ ↑↓	↑	9	Δ
8	↑↓ ↑↓ ↑↓	↑ ↑	13	↑↓ ↑↓ ↑↓	↑ ↑	13	0
9	↑↓ ↑↓ ↑↓	↑↓ ↑	16	↑↓ ↑↓ ↑↓	↑↓ ↑	16	0

further complicated by the large Jahn–Teller effects which occur in the spin-paired substances.

In high-spin complexes with $n \leqslant 5$ all electrons have parallel spins, and so there are just $\frac{n(n-1)}{2}$ pairs. In the high-spin complexes with $n > 5$ there are 5 electrons with one spin direction and $n - 5$ with the other. Hence the number of parallel pairs is

$$\frac{5(5-1)}{2} + \frac{(n-5)(n-6)}{2} = 10 + \frac{(n-5)(n-6)}{2}.$$

In the low-spin complexes with 4, 5, 6 and 7 electrons similar arguments show that there are just 3, 4, 6 and 9 pairs of electrons with parallel spin, respectively. If we denote the mean exchange energy for one pair of electrons by K we then get the exchange energies given in Table 3.3.1.

We can see from columns 3, 5 and 6 of Table 3.3.1 how big Δ must be for each *d* electron configuration in terms of *K*, in order to produce spin-pairing. A study of atomic spectral data shows that for a given transition-metal series and for ions of the same valency, *K* does not change very much, at least between near neighbour elements. We can, therefore, draw one very significant conclusion, namely that the configuration d^6 should form low-spin complexes at much lower Δ values than the d^4 or d^5 configurations. The ease of spin-pairing differs less for these last two configurations.

Our discussion thus far permits us to draw the following conclusions about the ease of spin-pairing in octahedrally coordinated compounds:

(1) For a given metal ion there is a critical value of the ligand-field at which the ground state changes from the high-spin to the low-spin configuration. Thus there should be some position in the series of ligands arranged according to increasing ligand-field strength such that all ligands to the right of this position induce spin-pairing and those to the left leave the ground state with maximum spin-multiplicity.

This statement is somewhat too strong, for we have neglected the influence of covalent bonding in reducing the repulsions between *d* electrons and hence facilitating spin-pairing. This effect should be particularly important for ions of high valency and perhaps also for ions of metals of the second and third transition series. It may have important quantitative consequences, but does not seem to spoil the qualitative validity of the simple argument.

(2) Within a given transition series and with ions of the same valency the ion with 6 *d* electrons should be induced to pair spins by ligands producing relatively small fields while the other ions require ligands further to the right in the ligand-field series.

(3) Ions of the metals of the second and third series should pair their spins more readily than those of the first series. This conclusion follows from the fact that Δ is larger in the second and third series. It is further strengthened by the independent observation that, as shown by studies of atomic spectra, the forces between *d* electrons are smaller for the larger transition-metal ions than for those of the first series. This means that forces *opposing* spin-pairing decrease as one goes from the first to the subsequent series.

Experimentally there is much evidence in support of each of these conclusions. For example the Fe^{2+} ion forms high-spin complexes with F^-, H_2O, aliphatic amines, etc., but low-spin complexes with phenanthrolines and the cyanide ion. Thus the critical position in the ligand-field series at which the change of configuration takes place is somewhere between ammonia and phenanthroline. On the other hand, the Mn^{2+} ion is induced to pair its spins only by the cyanide ion, that is the ion producing the highest ligand-field. This agrees with the conclusion that d^5 ions require higher ligand-fields than d^6 ions if they are to form low-spin complexes.

The situation with the corresponding trivalent ions is very similar. The Fe^{3+} ion is induced to pair its spins only by ligands with relatively high ligand-fields while the Co^{3+} ion is spin-paired in all of the complexes so far studied with the exception of the $[CoF_6]^{3-}$ ion. This again illustrates the ease with which d^6 ions pair their spins.

Comparison between the first and later transition series amply confirms our conclusion (3). While in the first series high-spin complexes are quite as common as low-spin ones, in the second and third transition series they are the exception. For example trivalent osmium compounds unlike the corresponding ferric complexes are usually spin-paired. On the other hand d^3 complexes are normal and paramagnetic in the second and third series just as they are in the first, showing that we are indeed dealing with the phenomenon of spin-pairing in the d^4, d^5 and d^6 cases, and not with some different effect of the high atomic number.

Finally we remark that the qualitative theory which we have developed here is an approximation to a more quantitative theory developed independently by a number of authors.[1, 3] This latter theory allows the critical Δ value needed for the spin-pairing of each ion to be calculated. It is found that these calculated Δ values agree as well as can be expected with the experimental Δ values of the ligands which are found to lie closest to the crossing points from high-spin to low-spin complexes.

3.4. Spin-pairing in non-octahedral complexes

The problem of spin-pairing in tetrahedral complexes is qualitatively similar to that for octahedral complexes. Ions with more than two *d* electrons and less than seven can have one of two different ground-state electron configurations depending on the strength of the crystal-field. One of these corresponds to the ground state of the free ion and has a maximum number of unpaired electrons; the other has a maximum number of electrons in the *e* orbital and a correspondingly lower number of unpaired spins as shown in Table 3.4.1.

TABLE 3.4.1

***d* electron arrangements in tetrahedral complexes**

n = number of unpaired spins

Number of *d* electrons	Arrangement in weak ligand-field		n	Arrangement in strong ligand-field		n
	e	*t*		*e*	*t*	
1	↑	—	1	↑	—	1
2	↑↑	—	2	↑↑	—	2
3	↑↑	↑	3	↑↓↑	—	1
4	↑↑	↑↑	4	↑↓↑↓	—	0
5	↑↑	↑↑↑	5	↑↓↑↓	↑	1
6	↑↓↑	↑↑↑	4	↑↓↑↓	↑↑	2
7	↑↓↑↓	↑↑↑	3	↑↓↑↓	↑↑↑	3
8	↑↓↑↓	↑↓↑↑	2	↑↓↑↓	↑↓↑↑	2
9	↑↓↑↓	↑↓↑↓↑	1	↑↓↑↓	↑↓↑↓↑	1

Quantitatively, however, the situation is very different for the two stereochemical arrangements, for the ligand-field is very much smaller in tetrahedral than in octahedral complexes as shown both by the interpretation of electronic spectra and by calculation. There is at present no evidence for spin-pairing in any tetrahedral complex of an ion of the first transition series.

Clearly the factors most likely to produce a spin-paired ion are:

(i) A ligand which produces a large field.

(ii) A metal ion of the third transition series preferably in a high valency.

(iii) The electron configuration which is most easily spin-paired.

The most easily paired configuration in a tetrahedral field is in fact the d^4 configuration, for this has just enough electrons to fill the stable *e* orbital (cf. d^6 with the t_{2g} orbital filled in octahedral environments). It may be significant that the compounds of the composition $MReCl_4$, where M is an alkali metal, are diamagnetic. If X-ray studies show them to contain the tetrahedral $[ReCl_4]^-$ ion they will be the first examples of spin-paired tetrahedral complexes.

For completeness we mention the spin-paired planar complexes of d^7 and d^8 ions here, although we shall delay any detailed discussion of them until the next chapter. In a planar complex the $d_{x^2-y^2}$ orbital is, as we have seen, much less stable than any other *d* orbital. Consequently with eight *d* electrons as in Ni^{+2}, Pd^{+2}, Pt^{2+}, Au^{3+}, etc., planar complexes may be found in which the d_{xy}, d_{xz}, d_{yz} and d_{z^2} orbitals are doubly occupied provided the energy separation between these orbitals and the $d_{x^2-y^2}$ orbital is large enough to induce spin-pairing. Similarly, d^7 ions may have all electrons in the lowest four orbitals. The preponderance of planar spin-paired d^8 ions in the later transitions series and their comparative rarity in the first can be explained in the same way as the greater frequency of spin-pairing in octahedral complexes of ions of the later series.

CHAPTER THREE

REVIEW REFERENCES

All of the general references to Section 2.2 deal also with the material of this chapter. See alao

3.2

JØRGENSEN, *Proceedings of the 10th Solvay Congress in Chemistry, Brussels, 1956*, p. 355

1. GRIFFITH, *J. Inorg. and Nucl. Chem.*, **2**, 229 (1956)
2. GRIFFITH, *Faraday Society Discussion*, **No. 26**, 81 (1958)
3. ORGEL, *J. Chem. Phys.*, **23**, 1819 (1955)

CHAPTER FOUR

Stereochemistry

4.1. Ionic coordination polyhedra

Before discussing the peculiarities of the stereochemistry of the transition metals we first examine the implications of a very much over-simplified ionic theory. We suppose that:

(1) Ions are charged, incompressible, non-polarizable spheres.

(2) An arrangement of ions of one charge about an ion of the opposite charge is stable only if the central ion is in contact with each of its neighbours. This places a lower limit on the ratio of the radius of the central ion to that of the surrounding ions for each type of coordination polyhedron, for if the central ion were too small it would 'rattle'. Since positive ions are almost always smaller than the negative ions which accompany them in crystals this restriction means effectively that the coordination number of small metal ions is often limited by the radius ratio rules, while the coordination number of anions is rarely limited in this way.

(3) The coordination number is as large as possible, subject to condition (2). Of course, the coordination number may also be restricted by the composition of the substance if it is necessarily present as discrete molecules, e.g. $TiCl_4$ in the gas phase.

(4) The arrangement of the coordinated groups minimizes the electrostatic repulsion energy between them.

It follows from (4) that an ideal ionic AB_2 complex should be linear, for this is the arrangement which maximizes the B–B distance and so minimizes the electrostatic repulsion between B groups. In a similar way the repulsion between B groups in AB_3 complexes is readily seen to be minimized if the molecule is planar and the B groups are at the vertices of an equilateral triangle. There are two other cases in which the preferred configuration depends only on symmetry, namely AB_4 and AB_6 complexes which should adopt regular tetrahedral and regular octahedral stereochemistries, respectively. These symmetry determined arrangements are illustrated in Fig. 4.1.1.

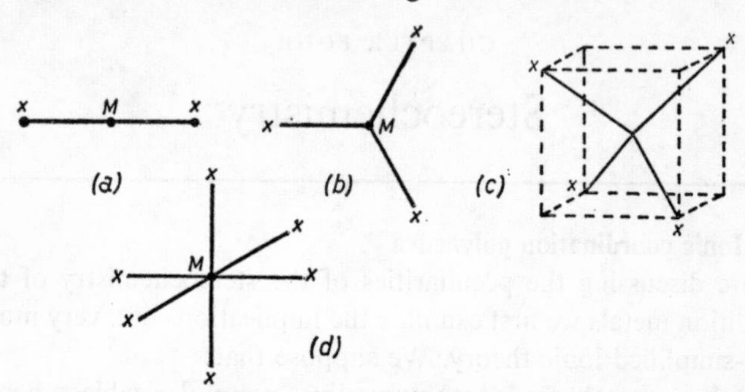

Fig. 4.1.1. Symmetry determined ionic coordination polyhedra, (a) linear MX_2, (b) equilateral triangular MX_3, (c) tetrahedral MX_4, (d) octahedral MX_6

In all other important cases the optimum configuration is not determined by symmetry alone. Although it is possible to arrange eight equivalent *B* groups at the vertices of a cube about a central *A* group as in Fig. 4.1.2*a*, this is not the configuration which minimizes the electrostatic repulsion energy, for clearly the square antiprism shown in Fig. 4.1.2*b* is more favourable.

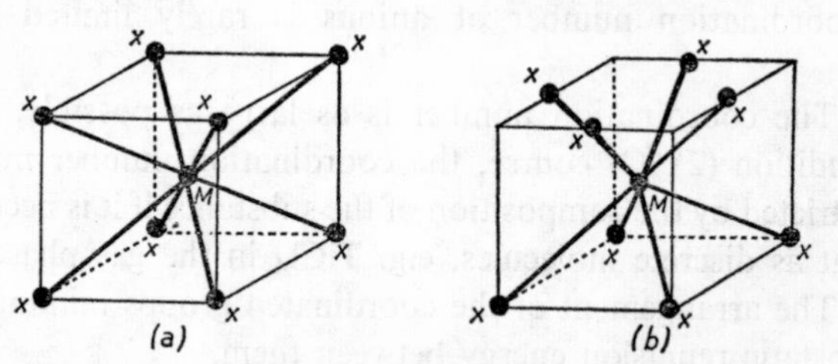

Fig. 4.1.2. Cubic and square antiprism arrangements for MX_8 groups

The only configurations of AB_5, AB_7 and AB_9 groups which maintain the equivalence of all *AB* bonds are the energetically unfavourable planar ones. Some of the configurations which lead to relatively favourable electrostatic energies are illustrated in Fig. 4.1.3. The two most important AB_5 configurations are the square pyramid and the trigonal bipyramid. Their electrostatic repulsion energies are very similar.

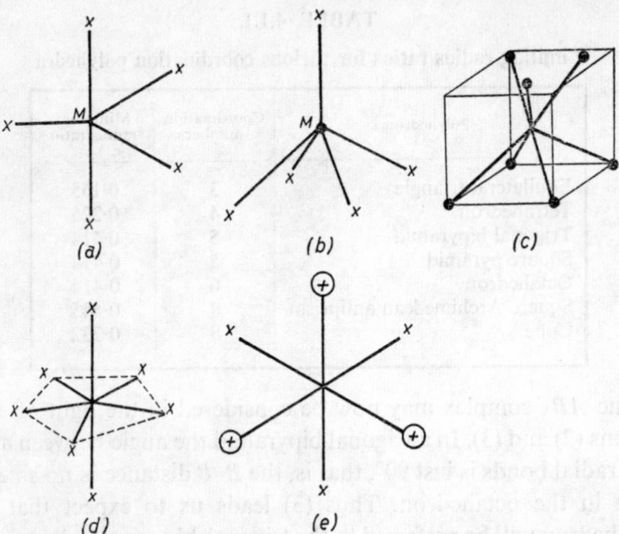

Fig. 4.1.3. Some favourable 5-, 7- and 9-fold coordinated structures. (a) Trigonal bipyramid, (b) square pyramid, (c) 4–3 coordination. (d) 7 coordination, (e) 9 coordination. We represent atoms above and below the plane of the paper by + and ○, respectively

So far we have made use of (4) to determine the ideal configuration for each type of AB_n complex. Now we must find the values of the ratio of the radii r_A and r_B of the A and B ions which are consistent with (2) and (3) for each coordination number. Clearly a linear AB_2 arrangement satisfies (2) for any value of the radius ratio. On the other hand, an elementary geometrical construction shows that in a planar, AB_3, complex, the A ion would 'rattle' inside the triangle of B ions if the ratio $\frac{r_A}{r_B}$ of the two ions were less than 0·155. Thus according to (2) a very small A ion cannot form an AB_3 complex with a large B ion, but must instead form an AB_2 complex. In the same way it follows that an AB_3 complex should only be stable if the radius ratio lies in the range $0{\cdot}155 \leqslant \frac{r_A}{r_B} \leqslant 0{\cdot}225$, for if $\frac{r_A}{r_B} \geqslant 0{\cdot}225$ the tetrahedral configuration is stable. Proceeding in this way, we derive the ranges of the radius ratio consistent with each type of coordination as shown in Table 4.1.1.

TABLE 4.1.1

Limiting radius ratios for various coordination polyhedra

Polyhedron	Coordination number	Minimum radius ratio
Equilateral triangle	3	0·155
Tetrahedron	4	0·225
Trigonal bipyramid	5	0·414
Square pyramid	5	0·414
Octahedron	6	0·414
Square Archimedean antiprism	8	0·645
Cube	8	0·732

The AB_5 complex may now be considered in the light of conditions (2) and (3). In a trigonal bipyramid the angle between axial and radial bonds is just 90°, that is, the B–B distance is no smaller than in the octahedron. Thus (3) leads us to expect that the octahedron will be preferred to the trigonal bipyramid. An exactly similar argument shows that the octahedron will also be preferred to a square pyramid. Thus except in isolated molecules or ions, we should not expect to find AB_5 arrangements.

This discussion shows that the widespread occurrence of regular tetrahedrally and octahedrally coordinated metal ions calls for no special interpretation in terms of bond hybridization, etc. It is rather the other four or six coordinated structures which require explanation; for example we shall need a special explanation of the widespread occurrence of planar coordination complexes of the compounds containing the Ni^{2+}, Pd^{2+} and Pt^{2+} ions.

These arguments from an electrostatic theory apply formally only to substances made up from monatomic ions. However, there is reason to believe that they are qualitatively correct in a much less restricted context. Thus, although it cannot be proved generally and rigorously, it is very plausible that regular octahedral and tetrahedral coordinations are the preferred arrangements for the disposition of most dipolar molecules or polyatomic anions around a central positive ion. They are simply the arrangements which place the ligands as far apart as possible, and since ligands usually repel one another they are to be expected if the metal ion behaves as a spherically symmetrical charge distribution. Thus the octahedral character of $[Co(NH_3)_6]^{3+}$ no more *implies* covalent bonding than does the octahedral environment of Na^+ in NaCl. Conversely the planarity of $[Pt(NH_3)_4]^{2+}$ requires comment in just the same way as does that of $[PtCl_4]^{2-}$.

4.2. The Jahn–Teller effect in octahedral complexes

We have seen that a regular octahedral environment is the most favourable one for a spherical positive ion surrounded by six negative ions or six dipolar molecules. We shall now establish a much more surprising result, namely that for certain ions with unfilled *d* electron shells the regular octahedral environment is necessarily *unstable*. There is no contradiction here, for we shall see that in a very real sense certain ions with unfilled *d* electron shells are not spherically symmetrical.

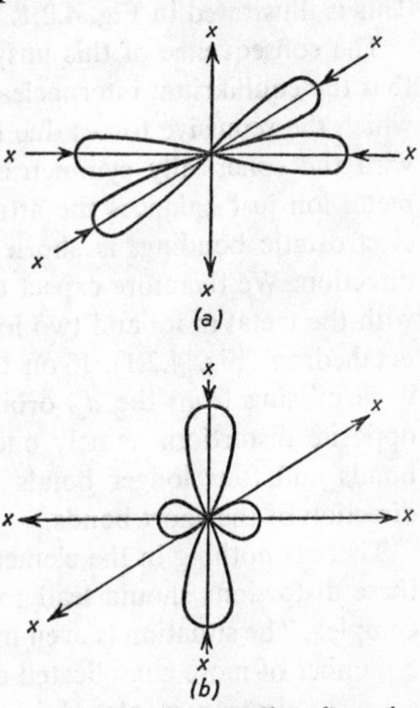

Fig. 4.2.1. Jahn–Teller distortion due to absence of a $d_{x^2-y^2}$ or d_{z^2} electron from the closed d^{10} shell. (a) The ligands in the xy plane are attracted owing to the less shielded nuclear attraction, (b) the ligands along the z axis are attracted

We may best illustrate the general theory by taking a particular example, that of the Cu^{2+} ion. The *d* electron configuration of this ion is $(t_{2g})^6(e_g)^3$ which, in an octahedral environment, gives rise to a doubly degenerate ground state since two assignments of the e_g electrons, $(d_{z^2})^2(d_{x^2-y^2})^1$ and $(d_{z^2})^1(d_{x^2-y^2})^2$, are possible.

Let us suppose that we try to introduce the Cu^{2+} ion in the $(t_{2g})^6(d_{z^2})^2(d_{x^2-y^2})^1$ configuration into a regular octahedral environment. We know that an ion with the configuration d^{10} is spherical. The ion which we are now considering differs from the d^{10} ion in that one electron has been removed from the $d_{x^2-y^2}$ orbital. Since this orbital is concentrated along the bond directions in the *xy* plane and has no electron density along the *z* axis, it follows that, if it is not filled, the ligands in the xy plane are attracted more strongly towards the nucleus than the ligands along the z axis. Stated in another way the removal of a $d_{x^2-y^2}$ electron from a d^{10} ion causes the resultant ion to lack spherical symmetry in such a way that the nucleus is less screened along the x and y directions than along the z direction. Consequently the ligands in the xy plane are attracted with a force equivalent to a larger apparent nuclear charge than that effective for the ligands along the z axis. This is illustrated in Fig. 4.2.1.

The consequence of this unsymmetrical attraction is naturally that the equilibrium internuclear distance, that is the distance at which the repulsive forces due to the overlap of ligand electrons with the spherically symmetrical inner electronic shells of the metal ion just balances the attractive force due to covalent and electrostatic bonding, is shorter in the xy plane than in the z direction. We therefore expect to find four short bonds coplanar with the metal atom and two longer ones completing a distorted octahedron (Fig. 4.2.1). If on the other hand the extra electron were missing from the d_{z^2} orbital we should expect an exactly opposite distortion, namely one to produce two short collinear bonds and four longer bonds in a plane perpendicular to the direction of the short bonds.

There is nothing in the elementary theory to indicate which of these distortions should lead to the greatest stabilization of the complex. The situation is even more unsatisfactory than this since a number of more complicated distortions are also possible if the extra e_g electron is placed in a linear combination of the d_{z^2} and the $d_{x^2-y^2}$ orbitals. Detailed calculations by Öpik and Pryce suggested that the situation with four short bonds should be stable in all cases,[1] but this result has been queried by Liehr and Ballhausen.[2] We shall see in the next section that experimentally, with at present a single exception, four short bonds and two long ones are observed. It is a curious and characteristic situation that one is able to predict with certainty that the octahedral environment is unstable and yet one is not able to predict with confidence the nature of the most stable distorted configuration.

Further insight into the nature of the distortions in these octahedral complexes of d^9 ions may be obtained by considering the way in which the energy levels of the d electrons change when the regular octahedron is distorted. Suppose we shorten four bonds in the xy plane and lengthen two in the z direction. Clearly this makes the $d_{x^2-y^2}$ less stable and the d_{z^2} orbital more stable, as shown in Fig. 4.2.2. The reverse distortion stabilizes the $d_{x^2-y^2}$ orbital at the expense of the d_{z^2} orbital. Theory shows that to a first approximation the stabilization of one orbital equals the destabilization of the other. Now if we have three electrons to place in the e_g orbitals it is clear that we gain an orbital energy $\frac{1}{2}\delta$ relative to the energy of the ion in the undistorted configuration by placing two electrons in the stable e_g orbital and only one in the unstable orbital, where δ is the difference in energy between the $d_{x^2-y^2}$ and d_{z^2} orbitals. It is this gain in orbital energy that provides the driving force for the distortion.

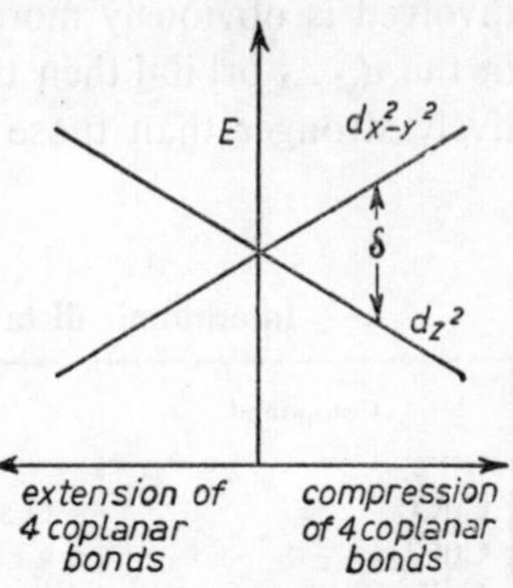

Fig. 4.2.2. Energies of the $d_{z^2-y^2}$ and d_{z^2} orbitals as a function of the distortion from regular cubic symmetry

The arguments of this section have depended only on there being an odd number of electrons in the e_g orbitals. Thus we expect distortions to give four short and two long bonds in the compounds of the following common metal ions:

d^4	$(t_{2g})^3(e_g)^1$	Cr^{2+}, Mn^{3+}	high spin
d^7	$(t_{2g})^6(e_g)^1$	Co^{2+}, Ni^{3+}	low spin
d^9	$(t_{2g})^6(e_g)^3$	Cu^{2+}, Ag^{2+}.	

Before looking in detail at the experimental evidence it is perhaps worth pointing out that planar complexes may be regarded as the limiting members of the class of distorted complexes, in which the two more weakly bound ligands have been removed completely. Later we shall see how the theory of the present section ties up with the remarks on planar d^7 and d^8 complexes which we made in Section 3.4.

The most studied of the ions which should distort strongly is undoubtedly the Cu^{2+} ion. It forms a very few tetrahedral complexes, e.g. K_2CuCl_4, but for the most part occurs in octahedral or planar environments. In the octahedral complexes one can almost invariably distinguish long from short bonds, and in all cases but that of K_2CuF_4, there are four short coplanar bonds. In K_2CuF_4 there are two short and four long bonds.[3] *

While we have developed our theory for the distortion of an originally regular octahedral environment, the structural principle involved is obviously more general. If the hole in the d shell is in the $d_{x^2-y^2}$ orbital then the bonds in the xy plane will be relatively stronger than those along the z axis, even if the ligands

TABLE 4.2.1

Interatomic distances in some Cu^{2+} compounds

Compound	Distances
CuO	4 O at 1·95 Å (square coplanar)
$CuCl_2$	4 Cl at 2·30 Å, 2 Cl at 2·95 Å
$CuBr_2$	4 Br at 2·40 Å, 2 Br at 3·18 Å
$CsCuCl_3$	4 Cl at 2·30 Å, 2 Cl at 2·64 Å
CuF_2	4 F at 1·93 Å, 2 F at 2·27 Å
(CrF_2)	4 F at 1·98–20·1 Å, 2 F at 2·43 Å
K_2CuF_4	
$Cu_2(OH)_2CO_3$	4 O (OH) at 1·98 Å, 2 O at 2·71 Å
$CuCl_2$—$2H_2O$	$2H_2O$ at 2·01 Å, 2 Cl at 2·31 Å, 2 Cl at 2·98 Å
K_2CuCl_4—$2H_2O$	$2H_2O$ at 2·01 Å, 2 Cl at 2·29 Å, 2 Cl at 2·93 Å
Cu(acetate)$_2$.H_2O	4 O at 1·97 Å, H_2O at 2·30 Å, Cu at 2·64 Å
Cu(formate)$_2$.$4H_2O$	4 O at 2·00 Å, 2 H_2O at 2·36 Å
Cu proline.$2H_2O$	2 N at 1·99 Å, 2 O at 2·03 Å, $2H_2O$ at 2·52 Å
$CuCl_2$.2 pyridine	2 N at 2·02 Å, 2 Cl at 2·28 Å, 2 Cl at 3·05 Å
$Cu(NH_3)_4SO_4.H_2O$	4 N at 2·05 Å, H_2O at 2·59 Å, H_2O at 3·37 Å
Cu—dimethylglyoxime	4 N at 1·94 Å, O at 2·43 Å
$Cu(NH_3)_2Cl_2$	2 N at 1·95 Å, 4 Cl at 2·76 Å
$Cu(NH_3)_2Br_2$	2 N at 2·03 Å, 4 Br at 2·88 Å

are not identical. In this way we can understand the structure of many more complex cupric compounds. In Table 4.2.1 we gather together some of the structural information on cupric compounds to illustrate our general arguments.

The Mn^{3+} has been studied in a number of compounds including MnF_3, the $[MnF_6]^{3-}$ ion, and Mn_3O_4. In each case the environment of the metal includes four short and two long bonds. Similarly the Cr^{2+} ion has been studied in CrF_2 which turns out

* Very recently two further examples of this type of distortion have been discovered in $MCrF_3$ and $MCuF_3$ compounds, where M is an alkali metal.

to have the same distorted rutile structure as CuF_2. The Ni^{3+} ion has been investigated in certain complex oxides such as $NaNiO_2$ and shown to have the low-spin configuration. It forms four short and two long bonds to oxide ions. The Co^{2+} ion is usually met with in the high-spin form, but the low-spin complexes which have been investigated are usually described as planar, although X-ray evidence is not available.

All of the ions which, from our simple model, we predict to distort have thus been found either in the characteristic distorted octahedral configuration or in the planar configuration. That this is indeed due to some mechanism concerned with the electronic configuration of the metal ion and not to the selection of appropriate examples from the massive literature of structural chemistry becomes clear if we consider series of analogous compounds. For example, the fluorides of the Fe^{2+}, Co^{2+}, Ni^{2+} and Zn^{2+} ions all have the rutile structure (Fig. 4.2.3) but Cr^{2+} and Cu^{2+} have rutile structures distorted in the now familiar way. This can hardly be connected with packing problems in the crystal for these would apply equally to all of the ions in such a series. Many other such series are now known, e.g. the series CrF_3, MnF_3 and FeF_3 of which only the Mn^{3+} compound is distorted, and a large series of mixed oxides having the spinel structure which distort if Cu^{2+} or Mn^{3+} occupy octahedral sites (or, as we shall see, if Ni^{2+} or Cu^{2+} occupy tetrahedral sites). From this it seems safe to conclude that the d^4, d^7 and d^9 ions are indeed different from other transition-metal ions in their stereochemical behaviour. Many further examples supporting this view are given in the review references.

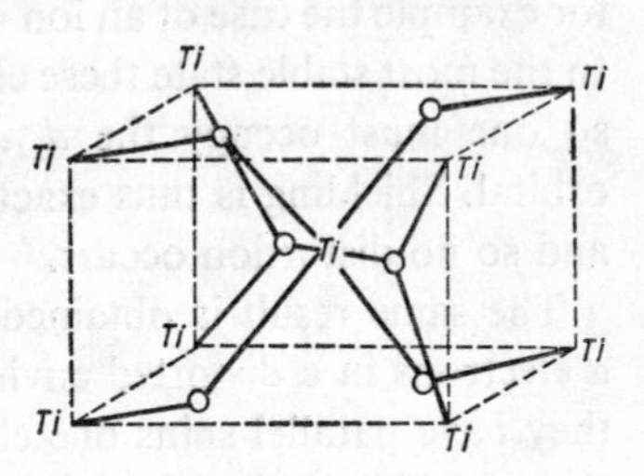

Fig. 4.2.3. The structure of rutile

We have in this section adopted implicitly an electrostatic interpretation of the Jahn–Teller distortions, but this was only for convenience of exposition. In the molecular-orbital theory, we remember that the e_g orbitals are antibonding; the $d_{x^2-y^2}$ orbital combines with the ligands in the xy plane while the d_{z^2} orbital combines most effectively with those along the z axis. It follows that if we have two antibonding electrons in the d_{z^2} and only one in the $d_{x^2-y^2}$ orbital, as in Cu^{2+}, the bonding will be strongest to the ligands in the *xy* plane. Hence just as in the electrostatic theory we expect four short coplanar bonds and two long bonds along the *z* axis. The reader may readily convince himself that the molecular-orbital theory leads to the same conclusions as the ionic theory in each of the examples which we have discussed. Thus stereochemistry gives no clue to the degree of covalency of the bonds formed by these ions.

We next consider ions with different numbers of *d* electrons in octahedral environments. First we note that filled and half-filled shells of *d* electrons cannot lead to distorted environments. Take for example the case of an ion with two electrons in the e_g orbitals. In the most stable state these electrons will have parallel spins and so one must occupy the $d_{x^2-y^2}$ orbital and the other the d_{z^2} orbital. Shielding is thus exactly equal along the *x*, *y* and *z* axes and so no distortion occurs.

The same result is obtained by considering the energy of two *d* electrons in a distorted environment (see Fig. 4.2.2). Provided they have parallel spins one electron is made unstable to exactly the same degree that the other is stabilized so that there is no nett energy effect and hence no tendency to distort. A precisely similar argument shows that the configuration $(t_{2g})^3$ is stable in an octahedral environment.

From this we deduce that to the approximation which we are working (neglect of spin-orbit interaction) no distortions are expected for high-spin d^3, d^5 or d^8 complexes or for low-spin d^6 complexes. None have been found.

Finally we must consider ions with t_{2g} shells which are neither filled nor half-filled, namely high-spin d^1, d^2, d^6 and d^7 ions and low-spin d^4 and d^5 ions. Fig. 2.2.1 shows that the t_{2g} orbitals interact much less strongly with the ligands than do the e_g orbitals. For this reason distortions due to the unsymmetrical occupation of the t_{2g} orbitals should be much smaller than those due to e_g orbital-degeneracy. Further detailed arguments confirm and strengthen this conclusion, although it is perhaps worth noting that with strongly double-bonding ligands somewhat larger distortions might be expected. Experimentally no unambiguous evidence for Jahn–Teller distortions in such ions is available, but there are some observations that suggest that small distortions may arise in this way. It seems unlikely that Jahn–Teller distortions due to t_{2g} electrons are ever responsible for gross stereochemical deviations from the predictions of the ionic theory.

4.3. Planar low-spin d^8 compounds

In Section 3.4 we saw that the existence of planar compounds of d^7 and d^8 ions is readily understood once it is realized that the $d_{x^2-y^2}$ orbital in a planar environment is much less stable than the other d orbitals. In the last section we saw that while low-spin d^7 ions in an octahedral environment do indeed tend to distort towards a planar configuration, no such tendency exists for high-spin d^8 ions in such a ligand field. Low-spin regular octahedral d^8 complexes should not exist. In this section we look more closely at these two situations to see the source of this clear-cut difference in behaviour.

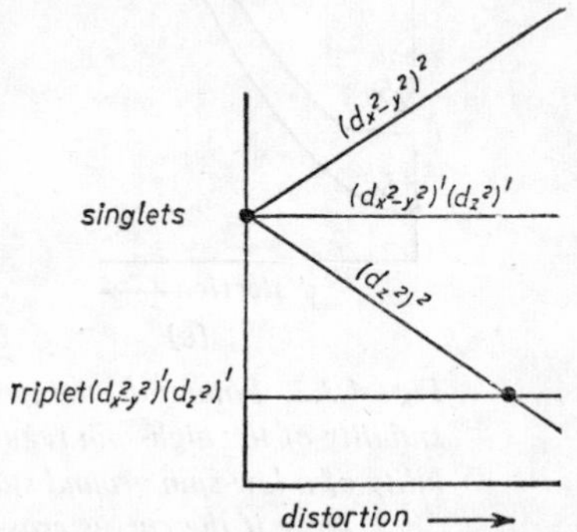

Fig. 4.3.1. Diagrammatic representation of the energies of $(t_{2g})^6(e_g)^2$ states in distorted octahedral (planar) surroundings

Consider first the effect of distorting progressively the environment of a d^8 ion on its energy levels. The lowest state in a regular octahedral field corresponds to $(t_{2g})^6(d_{z^2})^1(d_{x^2-y^2})^1$ with the spins of the unpaired electrons parallel. There are other states with the same orbital energy having the configurations $(t_{2g})^6(d_{z^2})^2$ and $(t_{2g})^6(d_{x^2-y^2})^2$, but since they have two e_g electrons with antiparallel spin they have less favourable exchange energies. When we distort the molecule the orbital energy of the ground state is unchanged, but that of certain of the excited states is strongly affected. If we shorten four bonds and lengthen two then the $(d_{z^2})^2$ configuration becomes more stable by δ $(2 \times \frac{1}{2}\delta)$ and the $(d_{x^2-y^2})^2$ configuration unstable by the same amount, as shown in Fig. 4.3.1 (cf. Fig. 4.2.2). As the distortion proceeds further δ increases until finally it must exceed the difference in exchange energy between the state with two parallel unpaired d electron spins and the lowest single (diamagnetic) state. When this happens the molecule passes from a high-spin to a low-spin configuration.

We see that *small* distortions of d^8 complexes are not to be expected. Distortion is an all or none process and whether it occurs or not depends on whether the upper spin-paired level can be depressed below the energy of the undistorted octahedral complex at its equilibrium internuclear distance or not. This is shown in Fig. 4.3.2. This figure differs from Fig. 4.3.1 in that the repulsion energy between closed shells has been included.

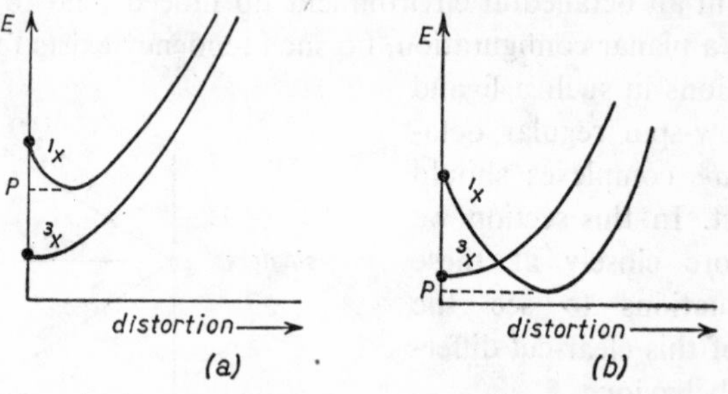

Fig. 4.3.2. Potential energy curve illustrating (a) the stability of the high-spin regular complex, (b) the possibility of a low-spin ground state. Note that distortion is large if the curves cross and zero otherwise

Clearly the cause of distortion in d^8 complexes is closely related to that in d^9 complexes, but differs in detail. In the former case all of the extra exchange energy of the high-spin state must be compensated for before a distorted structure becomes stable and so the *minimum* allowable distortion must counterbalance a definite loss of exchange energy. In the latter case the only force opposing distortion is the normal repulsive force between closed shells and since this is proportional to the distortion any magnitude of distortion is possible.

Turning now to d^7 ions we see that the situation is a little more complicated than we have previously indicated. Spin-paired d^7 ions must distort and since there is no loss of exchange energy on distortion there is no lower limit to the extent of distortion. On the other hand complexes which would not be spin-paired in the ground state may still occur as spin-paired planar complexes if the stabilization due to distortion is greater than the difference in energy between the undistorted high-spin and low-spin states. Thus d^7 ions, owing to the possibility of their existence as low-spin or high-spin regular octahedral complexes, are in some ways analogous to d^7 and in others to d^8 complexes with respect to their tendency to distortion. This situation does not arise for any other configuration.

4.4. Distortions in tetrahedral complexes

Distortions in tetrahedral complexes are relatively unimportant compared with those which we have already discussed. For completeness we give a rather condensed account of the theory. As we saw in Chapter 2 the unstable t_2 orbitals in tetrahedral complexes interact more strongly than the e orbitals with the ligands. Thus large distortions are expected only when we have 1, 2, 4 or 5

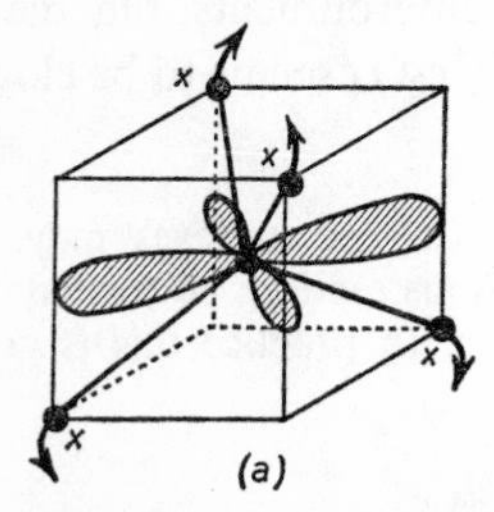

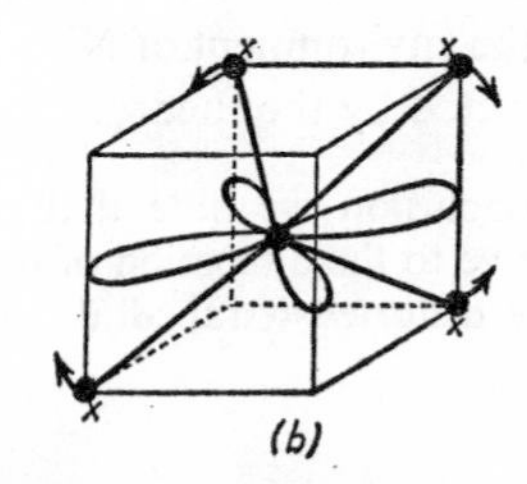

Fig. 4.4.1. Tetragonal distortions of tetrahedral environment. (a) elongation of the tetrahedron by a single t_2 electron for configurations d^3 and d^8, (b) flattening of the tetrahedron by a hole in the t_2 shell for configurations d^4 and d^9

electrons in the t_2 orbitals, i.e. for the high-spin d^3, d^4, d^8 and d^9 complexes.

The few cases in which tetrahedral complexes have been studied with sufficient care to detect distortions involve ions with the configurations d^8 and d^9, Ni^{2+} and Cu^{2+} respectively. In each case the distortion observed is such as to preserve tetragonal symmetry as shown in Fig. 4.4.1, so we shall consider only that situation. First, let us suppose that there is just one (or four) electrons in the t_2 orbital. Then if we take the tetragonal axis as the z axis it is clear that the d electron must be present in the d_{xy}

orbital. It then follows that the tetrahedron must elongate as shown in the figure, for the $d_{x^2-y^2}$ electron repels the ligands.

If we have two (or five) electrons in the t_2 orbital the situation is rather different. If tetragonal symmetry is to be maintained we must put the two electrons in the d_{xz} and d_{yz} orbitals and then the repulsion between electrons and ligands leads to a flattening of the tetrahedron towards a plane. This is most clearly seen by remembering that two electrons in the d_{xz} or d_{yz} orbital are equivalent to a positive hole in the d_{xy} orbital, since three electrons would just half fill the t_2 orbitals. Such a positive hole must attract the ligands as shown in Fig. 4.4.1*b*.

Experimentally it has been found that the tetrahedron of Cl^- ions about a Cu^{2+} ion in $[CuCl_4]^{2-}$ is flattened, while that in $[CoCl_4]^{2-}$ is much more nearly regular. Similarly the tetrahedral environment of the Cu^{2+} ion in $CuCr_2O_4$ is flattened, unlike those of Co^{2+} and Zn^{2+} in similar environments. On the other hand, the environment of Ni^{2+} in $NiCr_2O_4$ seems to be elongated as predicted by the theory.

In conclusion we note that planar Cu^{2+} complexes may, as an alternative to the discussion of the previous section, be treated as very strongly distorted tetrahedral complexes. In practice this is not very helpful.

4.5. Linear coordination of d^{10} ions

The simple ionic theory predicts that large ions such as the Ag^+, Au^+ and Hg^{2+} ions should always occur in environments of high coordination number. Crystallographic studies, however, show that many of the compounds of Cu^+, Ag^+ and particularly of Au^+ and Hg^{2+} contain linearly coordinated metal ions. For example, in $HgCl_2$ each Hg^{2+} ion is surrounded by two collinear near neighbour chloride ions and four more neighbours at much longer distances. Similarly Cu_2O and Ag_2O have a unique crystal-structure in which the metal ions are linearly coordinated. Hg^{2+} is hardly, if ever, found in a regular octahedral environment, although tetrahedral coordination is common.

It is often said that linear coordination indicates *sp* covalent bonding rather than ionic bonding. Even if one regards this as a satisfactory explanation of the facts one must clearly ask why

Hg^{2+}, for example, prefers to form *sp* bonds and Zn^{2+} and Cd^{2+} do not.

The *s* orbital of mercury is certainly a good deal more stable than those of zinc and cadmium. While this in itself would not favour *sp* linear bonding relative to octahedral coordination, but would rather increase the stability of both bonding arrangements more or less equally, in mercury the *s–p* energy separation is also large. Now a large *s–p* separation must indeed favour the formation of a small number of bonds each with a large *s* contribution rather than a large number of bonds each with a small *s* contribution. The *s–p* separations in Cu^+, Ag^+, Au^+ and Hg^{2+}, however, are not so much greater than in other related ions, and in my opinion are not large enough to account entirely for the considerable differences in stereochemistry.

TABLE 4.5.1

Energies (e.v.) of lowest d^9s states above the d^{10} ground state

	Cu^+	Zn^{2+}	Ag^+	Cd^{2+}	Au^+	Hg^{2+}	Tl^{3+}
d^9s	2·7	9·7	4·8	10·0	1·9	5·3	9·3

A second, and perhaps more important, mechanism involves *d–s* mixing. In Table 4.5.1 we show the *d–s* separations for the common d^{10} ions. It will be seen that a strong tendency to linear distortion is always associated with a small *d–s* separation. We believe that this is essentially because the mixing (hybridization) of *d* and *s* orbitals can lead to a charge distribution strongly favouring a linear arrangement by removing charge from the region between the ligands and the metal ion. In Fig. 4.5.1 we show diagrammatically the *d* and *s* orbitals and two *d–s* hybrids. By placing the two electrons which normally, in a d^{10} ion, occupy the d_{z^2} orbital in the $\frac{1}{\sqrt{2}}(d_{z^2} - s)$ hybrid orbital, charge is removed from the *z* axis and transferred to the *xy* plane. This can lead to the formation of very strong bonds along the *z* axis. In order to achieve this *d–s* mixing, however, one must promote electrons from the *d* to the next *s* orbital so that the whole process

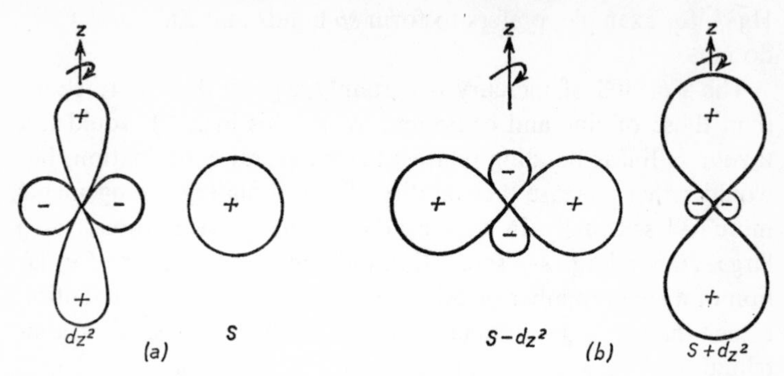

Fig. 4.5.1. (a) The d_{z^2} and s orbitals, (b) the $s - d_{z^2}$ and $s + d_{z^2}$ hybrid orbitals

of promotion and distortion is energetically advantageous only if the *d–s* separation is sufficiently small.

This effect is really closely related to the Jahn–Teller effect discussed in the previous sections, and the theory can be developed in the same way. There are, however, some important differences in detail between the two situations which have been discussed in the original papers.[4]

CHAPTER FOUR

GENERAL REFERENCES

DUNITZ and ORGEL, *Advances in Inorganic Chemistry and Radiochemistry*, Vol. II, 1960

NYHOLM, *Progress in Stereochemistry*, **1,** 322 (1954)

GILLESPIE and NYHOLM, *Progress in Stereochemistry*, **2,** 261 (1958)

WELLS, *Structural Inorganic Chemistry*. Oxford University Press, 1950

1. ÖPIK and PRYCE, *Proc. Roy. Soc. A.*, **238,** 425 (1957)
2. LIEHR and BALLHAUSEN, *Ann. Phys. (N.Y.)*, **3,** 304 (1958)
3. KNOX, *J. Chem. Phys.*, **30,** 991 (1959)
4. ORGEL, *J. Chem. Soc.*, 4186 (1958)

CHAPTER FIVE

Ionic Radii and the Stability of Transition-Metal Compounds

5.1. Ionic radii

In the absence of crystal-field effects the radii of the successive transition-metal ions would be expected to decrease steadily just as the radii of the rare earths decrease from lanthanum to lutecium. This is because an added *d* electron does not adequately shield the other *d* electrons from the increased nuclear charge associated with an increase in atomic number, and so the *d* orbitals should contract along a transition-metal series. Van Santen and van Weiringen were the first to point out that the deviations of the observed radii from this simple expectation receive a very simple qualitative interpretation if the angular distributions of the different *d* electrons are remembered.[1]

The t_{2g} electrons interact with and repel the ligands less strongly than do the e_g electrons. It follows that if we increase the nuclear charge by one unit and add a t_{2g} electron in going from a metal ion to its neighbour in the series we must expect a greater decrease in the ionic radius than if we add an e_g electron. Thus in high-spin complexes, large decreases in radius are expected as the first three *d* electrons are added to the t_{2g} orbital, then smaller decreases or even increases in radius as the fourth and fifth electrons go into the e_g orbital. The same pattern should then be followed as the next five electrons are added, one at a time. It will be seen from Fig. 5.1.1 that just such a variation is observed, but it should be remarked that the significance of the ionic radii given for d^4 and d^9 ions is not clear, since these ions do not occur in regular octahedral coordination. There seems to be no doubt that the ionic radii of the Mn^{2+} and Fe^{3+} ions lie above the expected smooth curve, as they should according to the ligand-field theory.

These arguments are readily extended to low-spin complexes.

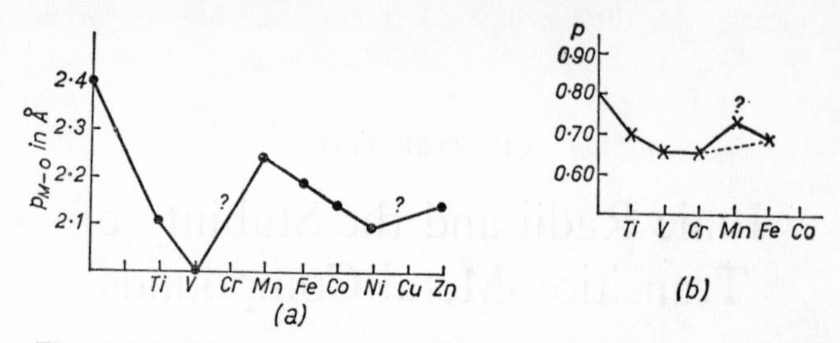

Fig. 5.1.1. (a) metal–oxygen distances in M.O. compounds,[2] *(b) ionic radii of trivalent transition-metal ions*[1]

Since the number of e_g electrons decreases on going from high-spin to the low-spin configuration the ionic radius should also decrease. This decrease should be very marked in d^5 and d^6 complexes.

The molecular-orbital theory interpretation of the same facts is also interesting. Since the t_{2g} orbital is a non-bonding orbital we may expect that the introduction of electrons into it will be without effect on the bond strength. Thus the ionic radii should decrease whenever, as we go along the periodic table, a t_{2g} electron is added to compensate for an increased nuclear charge. However, the e_g orbital is an antibonding orbital and when we add an electron to it there must be a reduction in bond strength. This leads to a lengthening of the metal–ligand bond which may or may not be larger than the average decrease in ionic radius which occurs between consecutive members of the transition series. If it is larger the ionic radius actually increases with atomic number, otherwise it decreases but to a lesser extent than usual. In a similar way the phenomenon of spin-pairing is always accompanied by the transfer of electrons from antibonding to non-bonding orbitals and so should lead to an increase in bond order and hence to a decrease in apparent ionic radius.

5.2. Ligand-field stabilizations

The lattice energies of ionic transition-metal compounds and the heats of formation of complex ions are clearly influenced by crystal-field effects. However, there is no direct way of measuring the ligand-field stabilization, for the quantity in which we are interested is the difference between the actual heat of formation and the heat of formation which we would get if no crystal-field effects were present. We can measure the first quantity but obviously we cannot measure the second.

The procedure which we must adopt is therefore an indirect one which depends on the estimation of ligand-field stabilizations from Δ values determined spectroscopically. We know that the energies of the t_{2g} and e_g orbitals relative to the mean d electron energy in an octahedral environment are $-\frac{2}{5}\Delta$ and $\frac{3}{5}\Delta$ respectively. Thus if the ground state corresponds to the configuration $(t_{2g})^p(e_g)^q$ its ligand-field energy is just $(-\frac{2}{5}p+\frac{3}{5}q)\Delta$. In the absence of orientation of electrons in the ligand-field there would naturally be no stabilization, for there would be $\frac{3}{5}n$ electrons in the t_{2g} and $\frac{2}{5}n$ electrons in the e_g orbitals. Thus, with certain reservations to be discussed, $(-\frac{2}{5}p+\frac{3}{5}q)\Delta$ is a measure of the ligand-field stabilization in octahedral complexes. In Table 5.2.1 we give this quantity

TABLE 5.2.1

Ligand-field stabilizations in octahedral and tetrahedral environments

Number of d electrons	Octahedral complex	Tetrahedral complex
1, 6	$-\frac{2}{5}\Delta$	$-\frac{3}{5}\Delta$
2, 7	$-\frac{4}{5}\Delta$	$-\frac{6}{5}\Delta$
3, 8	$-\frac{6}{5}\Delta$	$-\frac{4}{5}\Delta$
4, 9	$-\frac{3}{5}\Delta$	$-\frac{2}{5}\Delta$
0, 5, 10	0	0

for the different high-spin configurations and also the corresponding quantities for tetrahedral environments. It should be noted that these values are found by assigning integral numbers of electrons to the t_{2g} and e_g orbitals for all configurations and are therefore somewhat inaccurate for octahedrally coordinated d^2 and d^7 ions and for tetrahedrally coordinated d^3 and d^8 ions (Chapter 6).

The values given in Table 5.2.1 are only approximate for another reason. We have supposed that the crystal-field stabilization is the total ligand-field energy as calculated from optical data. This cannot be quite true, because the effect of the ligand-field stabilization on the ionic radius has been neglected. In fact part of the ligand-field energy is used up in overcoming the normal repulsive forces in the crystal and thus decreasing the ionic radius slightly. This effect is likely to be quite small and is rather difficult to discuss quantitatively.[2]

While the ligand-field stabilizations given in Table 5.2.1 are directly relevant to the observed thermodynamic quantities for most ions this is not the case for octahedrally coordinated d^4 and d^9 ions, since these are further stabilized by the Jahn–Teller distortions. Thus crystal-field effects as given in Table 5.2.1 have been underestimated for the important cases of the Cr^{2+} and Cu^{2+} ion by an amount which cannot be calculated at present.

Turning now to the experimental evidence we find that the heats of hydration of the divalent transition-metal ions do not fall on a smooth curve, but show a distinct minimum at Mn^{2+}. Since the Mn^{2+} ion is also the one with the minimum ligand-field energy this suggests that the two phenomena may be connected. If the calculated crystal-field stabilizations, obtained using spectroscopic Δ values, are subtracted from the hydration energies it is found that the resultant hydration energies corrected for ligand-field effects do fall on a smoother curve (Fig. 5.2.1*a*). Similarly a smooth curve is obtained for the trivalent ions only after allowing for crystal-field effects (Fig. 5.2.1*b*).

These observations suggest the following hypothesis:

In the absence of ligand-field effects the thermodynamic properties of transition-metal compounds, or at least their heats of formation, would evolve steadily along the transition series, for example from Ti^{2+} to Zn^{2+}.

It should be noted that we do not say that all differences between ions are due to crystal-field effects. The stabilities, for example, rise steadily from Ti^{2+} to Zn^{2+} *after correction for ligand-field effects*. This is no doubt connected with the decrease in ionic radius and concomitant increase in electronegativity which occurs as one goes along the series. It is only the discontinuities in the steady evolutions of the heats of hydration, etc., which can be attributed to ligand-field effects. Even this is a somewhat controversial point to which we must return later.

Granting for the moment the hypothesis which we have put forward we can now understand why the 'double-humped' curve

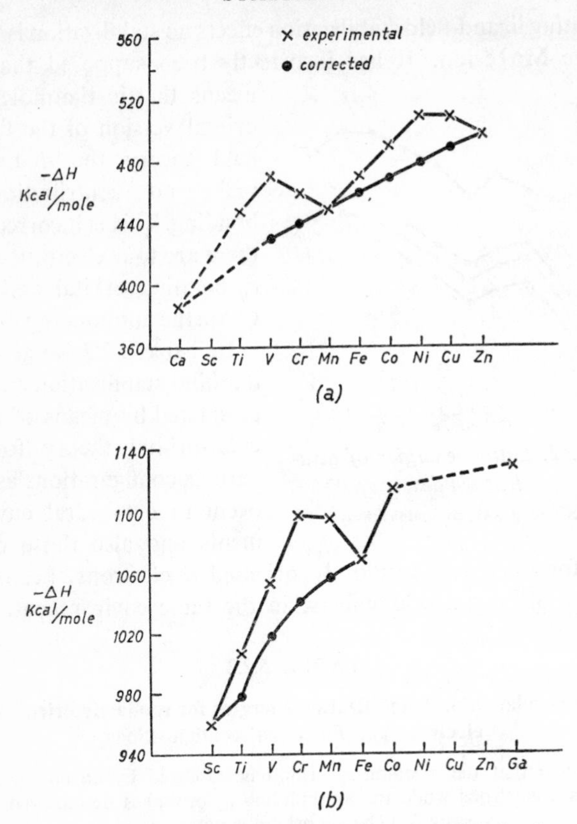

Fig. 5.2.1. Empirical and corrected heats of hydration (a) for divalent ions, (b) for trivalent ions

(McClure, private communication)

which we have found for the hydration energies of ions is also found for the lattice energies of a great variety of transition-metal compounds as shown for a few selected examples in Fig. 5.2.2.

The stabilization effects are much smaller in tetrahedral complexes than in octahedral ones owing to the very different values of the crystal-field splitting. Furthermore, the experimental evidence is not nearly as extensive. We shall see in Section 5.4 that there is nevertheless strong qualitative evidence that ligand-field stabilizations are also important in tetrahedral environments.

Some confusion has arisen in the past from the fact that in

estimating ligand-field stabilization effects no stabilization is found for the Mn^{2+} ion. It has incorrectly been supposed that this means that in the molecular-orbital version of the ligand-field theory the d orbitals make no contribution to bonding. This is incorrect, for there are four electrons in the e_g bonding orbital and only two in the antibonding orbital.

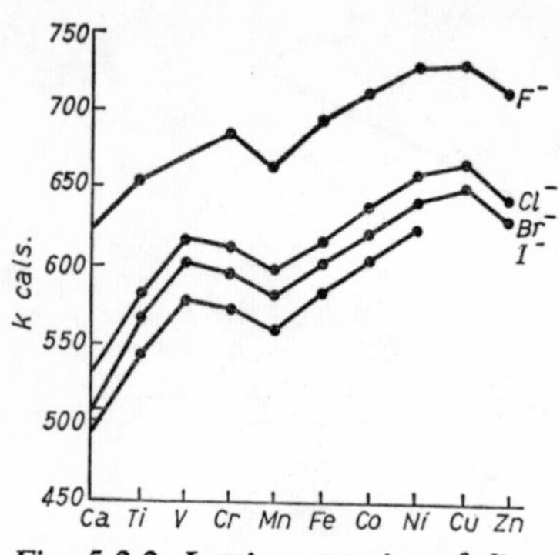

Fig. 5.2.2. Lattice energies of divalent halides

(McClure, private communication)

In Table 5.2.2 we give the d orbital stabilization energies calculated by means of molecular-orbital theory for the various configurations as they occur in octahedral environments and also those calculated for ions with randomly oriented d electrons, i.e. in the absence of crystal-field effects, in the same environment. It is

TABLE 5.2.2

Molecular orbital stabilization energies for randomly oriented electrons and for actual configurations

We assume that the bonding e_g orbital is stabilized by an energy Δ and contains 4 electrons while the antibonding e_g orbital is destabilized by an energy Δ. (The t_{2g} orbital is non-bonding)

Number of d electrons	Molecular-orbital stabilization if d electrons randomly oriented	Molecular-orbital stabilization of actual configuration	Ligand-field stabilization
0	4Δ	4Δ	0
1	$\frac{18}{5}\Delta$	4Δ	$\frac{2}{5}\Delta$
2	$\frac{16}{5}\Delta$	4Δ	$\frac{4}{5}\Delta$
3	$\frac{14}{5}\Delta$	4Δ	$\frac{6}{5}\Delta$
4	$\frac{12}{5}\Delta$	3Δ	$\frac{3}{5}\Delta$
5	2Δ	2Δ	0
6	$\frac{8}{5}\Delta$	2Δ	$\frac{2}{5}\Delta$
7	$\frac{6}{5}\Delta$	2Δ	$\frac{4}{5}\Delta$
8	$\frac{4}{5}\Delta$	2Δ	$\frac{6}{5}\Delta$
9	$\frac{2}{5}\Delta$	Δ	$\frac{3}{5}\Delta$
10	0	0	0

clear that the latter vary steadily through the series and so can legitimately be included in the steady increase of stability along the series when considering ligand-field effects. This is why we do not take account of them explicitly in our discussion of the effect of *d* electrons on the thermodynamic properties of complexes.

5.3. The extra stability of low-spin complexes

Low-spin complexes of d^5 and d^6 ions are generally thought of as being more stable than corresponding high-spin complexes. This is indeed quite correct, but it is necessary to analyse the situation rather carefully in order to differentiate between the different factors involved.

Firstly, there is a purely kinetic factor. For reasons which we shall discuss at length in Chapter 7 octahedral low-spin d^6 complexes are peculiarly inert with respect both to substitution and to oxidation–reduction reactions. This has often led to the impression that the compounds are more stable thermodynamically than is actually the case. On the other hand, the mere fact that the ground state of a complex has the low-spin configuration guarantees that it is more stable than it would be in the absence of spin-pairing, for the high-spin state is now above the ground state in energy.

The extra stability of the spin-paired state need not be much greater than kT, that is greater than a very few Kcals. However, once the cross-over point for spin-pairing has been passed the extra stabilization of a spin-paired complex increases rapidly, for example the excess ligand-field stabilization for a d^6 ion increases as 2Δ, so that in most cases the effect will in fact be appreciable. An exception is the $[Co(H_2O)_6]^{3+}$ ion which, although spin-paired, lies so close to the crossing-point that it can hardly be stabilized by more than 5 Kcals. at the most.

A more complete discussion of the effect of spin-pairing on stability requires us to take account of the change of ionic radius and hence of Δ which occurs when the ground-state configuration is changed. We illustrate the potential energy curves for high-spin and low-spin complexes in Fig. 5.3.1 (note that the low-spin state always has its energy minimum at a smaller internuclear distance than the high-spin state). In Fig. 5.3.1*a* and *c* we have the simple situations with high- and low-spin states as the ground states,

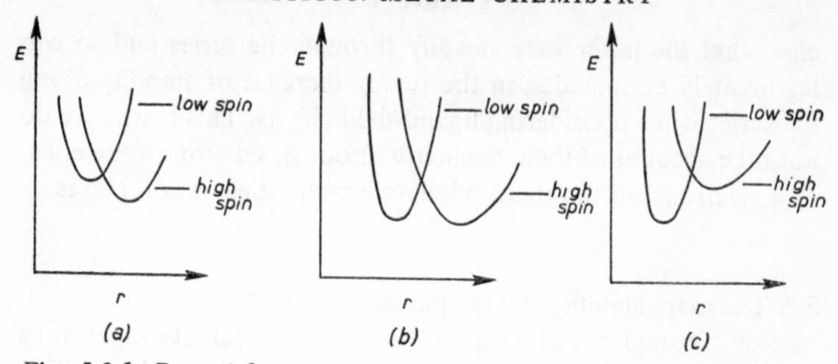

Fig. 5.3.1. Potential energy curves for (a) high-spin, (b) equilibrium, (c) low-spin complexes.

respectively. In Fig. 5.3.1*b* we have an interesting intermediate situation when the energy minima of the high and low-spin states are sufficiently close together for an equilibrium between them to exist at room temperature. When this happens the magnetic properties and the absorption spectra vary in a highly anomalous way with the temperature. Such effects have been observed, particularly for a variety of porphyrin derivations of the Fe^{2+} and Fe^{3+} ions and for Co^{3+} oxides.

We have seen that, almost by definition, a low-spin complex is stabilized by spin-pairing. We must remember, however, that our reference state is the hypothetical high-spin state of the same complex. We must not deduce that a low-spin complex is thermodynamically more stable than high-spin complexes of other metal ions.

5.4. The relative stability of tetrahedral and octahedral configurations[3, 4]

The general point of view developed in this chapter suggests that in the absence of crystal-field effects, the relative stability of octahedral and tetrahedral complexes should vary smoothly through any series of high-spin transition-metal complexes. That this is not the case may be seen by considering the sequence of ions Co^{2+}, Ni^{2+}, Cu^{2+} and Zn^{2+}. The Zn^{2+} ion has a very strong tendency to appear in tetrahedral environments as is indicated by its forming a tetrahedrally coordinated oxide and the tetrahedral $[Zn(NH_3)_4]^{2+}$ ion, etc. The Cu^{2+} ion is only known in a tetrahedral environment in the $[CuCl_4]^{2-}$ ion and in a few mixed oxides. The Ni^{2+} ion similarly forms tetrahedral complexes only in exceptional cases; the known tetrahedrally coordinated substances are $(PPh_3)_2NiCl_2$, $NiCr_2O_4$ and a complex tetraphenyl arsonium salt of the $[NiCl_4]^{2-}$ ion. The Co^{2+} ion, however, forms tetrahedral complexes quite readily; almost all of the many bright blue Co^{2+} compounds are tetrahedrally coordinated.

Qualitatively the reason for this is readily seen from Table 5.2.1. The ligand-field stabilization of the octahedral complexes of these ions rises to a maximum at Ni^{2+} (d^8), but the stabilization of tetrahedral complexes has its maximum value at Co^{2+} (d^7) and then falls by $\frac{2}{5}\Delta$ on going on to Ni^{2+}. Thus the steady increase of the tendency to form tetrahedral complexes which is apparent from a comparison of Mn^{2+} with Zn^{2+}, neither of which is affected by crystal-fields, is interrupted on going from Co^{2+} to Ni^{2+}. In fact at this point the ligand-field contribution to the energy difference between octahedral and tetrahedral complexes changes by $\frac{2}{5}(\Delta_{oct.} + \Delta_{tetr.})$.

The value of Δ for octahedral environments is so much larger than that for tetrahedral that it will usually dominate the 'site-preference energy'. But in the case of the Co^{2+} ion the stabilization energy in tetrahedral sites is by no means negligible. This theory may be put to a fairly rigorous test by considering the distribution of cations in the spinels.

The spinels are complex oxides having the formula $M^{2+}M_2^{3+}O_4$ where M^{2+} may be Mg^{2+}, Mn^{2+}, Fe^{2+}, Co^{2+}, Ni^{2+}, Cu^{2+}, Zn^{2+}, etc., and M^{3+} may be Al^{3+}, Cr^{3+}, Mn^{3+}, Fe^{3+}, Co^{3+}, etc. The regular structure consists of an almost close-packed lattice of oxide ions in which $\frac{1}{3}$ of the metal ions are accommodated at tetrahedral sites and the rest at octahedral sites (Fig. 5.4.1). A spinel is said to be normal if the M^{2+} ions occupy the tetrahedral sites and the M^{3+} ions the octahedral sites, inverted if the M^{3+} ions occupy the tetrahedral and half the octahedral sites and the M^{2+} ions the remaining octahedral sites, and partially inverted otherwise.

It is found, for example, that Mn_3O_4 is a normal spinel but Fe_3O_4 is inverted. We can see why this is if we remember that the Mn^{3+} but not the Mn^{2+} ion is stabilized by a crystal-field and hence will tend to go to the site which provides the maximum

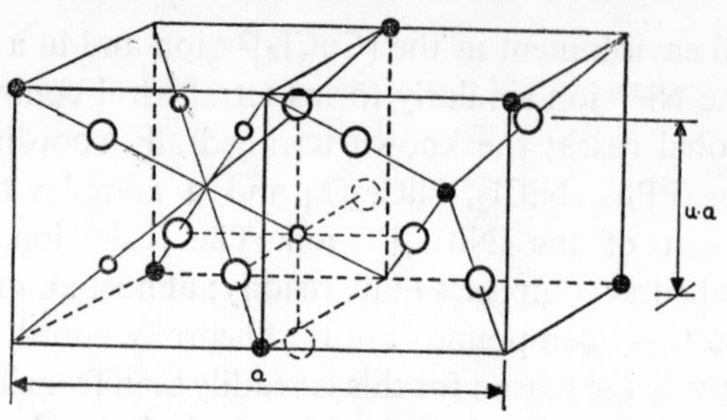

Fig. 5.4.1. The structure of spinel

crystal-field stabilization, that is the octahedral site. On the other hand, Fe^{2+} is sensitive to crystal-fields but Fe^{3+} is not, so that it is now the divalent ion which goes to the octahedral site. Thus in Mn_3O_4 the trivalent ion occupies the octahedral sites but in Fe_3O_4 half of these are occupied by the Fe^{2+} ions.

The argument given qualitatively above may be made semi-quantitative in terms of site-preference energies if Δ is known with sufficient accuracy for the various ions concerned, at each of the two kinds of sites. When site-preference energies are calculated using optically determined Δ values a rather good agreement between the calculated and observed degrees of inversion is obtained.

We see that ligand-field effects can sometimes lead to a complex acquiring a stereochemistry such that the metal ion has just enough stable orbitals to accommodate all of its electrons. In this connexion the structure of the $[Mo(CN)_8]^{4-}$ ion (Fig. 2.2.4) is particularly interesting. The arrangement of CN^- ions is such as to stabilize just one *d* orbital relative to all the others (Fig. 2.2.2*d*). This presumably is why the structure is adopted only by metal ions with one or two *d* electrons.

5.5. The effect of electronegativity[5, 6]

In the foregoing discussion of the stability of transition-metal compounds we have only made passing mention of the effect of electronegativity. This is a difficult topic, but unfortunately must be tackled if the point of recent discussions of the stability of complex ions in solution are to be appreciated. The same general considerations are also relevant to our previous sections on lattice energies, etc.

In so far as the bonding between metal ions and ligands is due to the donation of electrons from the ligands to the metal ion we may expect the strength of the ligand-metal bond to increase with the electron-attracting power of the metal ion. In the case of transition-metal compounds electrons may be accepted by the *d*, *s* or *p* orbitals so that there are really three relevant electron affinities. To simplify our discussion we shall consider only the *d* and *s* orbitals.

In Table 5.5.1 we have collected together the energies for some

TABLE 5.5.1

Electron affinities in electron volts of divalent transition-metal ions (*a*) for a pair of *s* electrons, (*b*) for one *d* electron

	s electron affinity	*d* electron affinity
Ti^{++}	20·46	13·5
V^{++}	20·94	14·2
Cr^{++}	22·2	16·49
Mn^{++}	23·07	13·4
Fe^{++}	24·08	16·0
Co^{++}	24·91	17·0
Ni^{++}	25·78	18·1
Cu^{++}	27·5	20·3
Zn^{++}	27·35	—

relevant electronic processes, namely $M^{2+}(d^n) + 2e \longrightarrow M(d^ns^2)$ for the *s* electron affinity and $M^{2+}(d^n) + e \longrightarrow M^+(d^{n+1})$ for the *d* electron affinity. The justification for regarding the first of the quantities as giving the best measure of the affinity for *s* electrons is not very good, and the process $M^{2+}(d^n) + e \longrightarrow M^+(d^ns)$ in which one *s* electron is gained has sometimes been considered instead. The reader is referred to the references for detailed discussion.[5,6] It should be noticed that the energy of the process $M^{2+}(d^n) + 2e \longrightarrow M(d^ns^2)$ is just the sum of the first two ionization potentials of the neutral atom when this has the configuration d^ns^2, but is somewhat different for chromium and copper which have the d^5s and $d^{10}s$ configurations, respectively.

It will be seen that the *s* electron affinity increases quite steadily along the series from Ti^{2+} to Cu^{2+} and falls only slightly to Zn^{2+}, but that the *d* electron affinity has a sharp maximum at Cr^{2+} (d^4) and rises steadily from Mn^{2+} (d^5) to Cu^{2+} (d^9). One may then ask if any or all of the stabilization which we have attributed to crystal-field effects are really due to electronegativity effects, since the electron affinity for *d* electrons is minimal at the d^5 configuration and maximal at the d^4 and d^9 configurations.

My own view is that though the effect of electronegativity is a very important one, most of it has been allowed for once the steady variation of corrected heats of formation from Mn^{2+} to Zn^{2+} has been considered; crystal-field effects are important in the compounds of Fe^{2+}, Co^{2+} and Ni^{2+} ions and dominant in those of the Cu^{2+} ion. However, this view is not accepted by everyone.

5.6. Complex ions in solution

When we consider the stability of complex ions in aqueous solution we are concerned not with the formation of these ions from their components but with replacement reactions

$$[M(H_2O)_6]^{n+} + pL \rightarrow [M^{n+}(H_2O)_q L_p] + (6-q)H_2O,$$

in which a certain number of ligand molecules expel an equal or lesser number of water molecules from the first coordination sphere around the metal ion.

The heat of such a reaction can be thought of as made up of two parts. The first is the corrected heat of reaction* which would vary smoothly through a series of transition-metal complexes of a given ligand were it not for ligand-field and electronegativity effects. The second is the difference between the crystal-field energy for the hydrate and for the complex ion (and also any energy arising from electronegativity effects which is not considered in the first part).

We see in a general way that crystal-field effects promote reactions if the ligand-field produced by the reagent is greater than that produced by water, and if the metal ion is sensitive to crystal-field stabilization. The Mn^{2+} and Zn^{2+} systems, which are unaffected by ligand-field splittings, provide, as usual, a convenient pair of systems from which to determine the general trend of the corrected heats of reaction throughout the first series.

Ligands which coordinate through oxygen usually produce crystal-fields quite similar to those of the water molecule and so the stability of their complexes will not be much affected by ligand-field effects, while complexes formed by the amines and other ligands which produce large fields may be strongly stabilized. Thus we expect the Ni^{2+} ion, which is stabilized more than any other ion in regular octahedral complexes, to show an unusually

* By this we mean the difference between the corrected heats of formation (as discussed in Section 5.2) of the complex and the hydrate.

high affinity for amines relative to water when compared with, say, Mn^{2+} which is unaffected by ligand-fields. This and other similar qualitative conclusions are verified experimentally, for example the ammines of Ni^{2+} are very much more stable than those of Mn^{2+} with respect to hydrolysis.

The quantitative data with which to test the predictions of the theory are not directly available. The ligand-field effects produce contributions to ΔH, the heat of complex formation, but by far the greater number of the experimental data refer to equilibrium constants for reactions in aqueous solution, and so give directly ΔF values for the reactions. In order to use these latter for comparison with ligand-field calculations it is necessary to make some assumptions about the way the entropy of reaction varies between corresponding reactions of different ions. We usually suppose that this variation may be ignored in comparisons of the type which we shall make.

In Table 5.6.1 we present some typical values for the successive formation constants of complexes of the divalent ions of the first series. First we shall comment on some distinctive qualitative features of these data. Normally the successive stability constants for the formation of complexes by a given ligand with a given metal ion fall off steadily from K_1 to K_6. This is partly due to a statistical effect, namely that the number of available water molecules which may be replaced by the ligand decreases as the number of ligand molecules already in the complex increases. This statistical effect, however, does not account for all the variation and it must be supposed that there is also a saturation effect in the sense that each ligand in the complex makes it more difficult to replace further water molecules by the same ligand. This effect must be electronic in origin. We can perhaps say that the strongly coordinating ligands such as ammonia donate electrons somewhat more effectively than water. After a few ligand molecules have replaced water molecules the electron affinity of the metal has been satisfied rather more than in the hydrate so the advantage of coordinating further molecules which are stronger electron donors than water is lessened.

The Cu^{2+} ion is remarkable for the sudden sharp drop in stability which occurs between K_4 and K_5. This is undoubtedly connected with the Jahn–Teller effect, that is with the tendency of the

TABLE 5.6.1

Stability constants for some metal complexes in aqueous solution

Ligand		Mn^{2+}	Fe^{2+}	Co^{2+}	Ni^{2+}	Cu^{2+}	Zn^{2+}
NH_3	K_1			2·11	2·79	4·15	2·37
	K_2			1·63	2·24	3·50	2·44
	K_3			1·05	1·73	2·89	2·50
	K_4			0·76	1·19	2·13	2·15
	K_5			0·18	0·75	−0·52	
	K_6			−0·62	0·03		
Ethylene-diamine	K_1	2·73	4·28	5·89	7·52	10·55	5·71
	K_2	2·06	3·25	4·83	6·28	9·05	4·66
	K_3	0·88	1·99	3·10	4·26	−1·0	1·72
Imidazole	K_1					4·37	2·58
	K_2					3·57	2·37
	K_3					2·85	2·23
	K_4					2·06	2·02
Oxalate	K_1	3·82	4·7	4·7		8·5	4·68
	K_2						2·36
Salicyl aldehyde	K_1	3·73	4·22	4·67	5·22	7·40	4·50
	K_2	3·06	3·40	3·63	3·97	5·91	3·60
Hydroxide	K_1	2·83		3·6	3·8	7·8	4·5
Salicylic acid	K_1					10·6	

Cu^{2+} ion to form four strong bonds in a plane and then two much weaker ones, to complete a distorted octahedron. It is particularly interesting that recent measurements on the ammines of the Cr^{2+} ion show that in this case too the first four formation constants vary in the normal way, but that there is a sharp drop on going from K_4 to K_5. These facts are not easily explained except in terms of the characteristic Jahn–Teller distortion of d^4 and d^9 ions.

Another curious anomaly is the increase of K from K_1 to K_3 for the ammines of Zn^{2+} and the subsequent drop to K_4, followed by a much more rapid drop thereafter. This too receives an explanation in terms of the stereochemical tendencies of the metal ion concerned. The Zn^{2+} ion more than any other of the group is stable in tetrahedral environments. It seems that in aqueous solutions $[Zn(H_2O)_6]^{2+}$ is the predominant species (perhaps due to the enormous excess of water). In the series of ammines the $[Zn(NH_3)_4]^{2+}$ is especially stable, although $[Zn(NH_3)_6]^{2+}$ can be formed if the ammonia concentration is high enough.

Since the octahedral configuration is stable with no ammonia present and the tetrahedral when four ammonia molecules are present we may expect a steady changeover in the relative stability of octahedral and tetrahedral environments as the number of ammonia molecules increases. Now all of the usual methods of determining these equilibrium constants measure the sum of the formation constants for tetrahedrally and octahedrally coordinated complexes containing a fixed number of ligands. In the case of the Zn^{2+} ion we may suppose that K is made up of two parts. The first, K^{oct}, decreases from K_1 to K_6 and corresponds to the usual reaction

$$[Zn^{2+}(H_2O)_6] + nL \rightarrow [Zn^{2+}(H_2O)_{6-n}L_n] + nH_2O.$$

The second, K^{tetr}, increases from a small value for K_1 to a larger one for K_4 since it corresponds to the reaction

$$[Zn^{2+}(H_2O)_6] + nL \rightarrow [Zn^{2+}(H^2O)_{4-n}L_n] + (n+2)H_2O$$

and we expect the relative stability of the tetrahedral configuration to increase with n. The observed behaviour of the total K for Zn^{2+} can now be understood. The increase in K between K_1 and K_2, and between K_2 and K_3, is due to the increasing stability of the tetrahedral complex relative to the octahedral; the sharp fall after K_4 is due to the fact that K_5 and K_6 *must* correspond to octahedral complexes.

A number of other anomalies have similar origins. For example, K_2 is greater than K_1 for the ammines of Ag^+ owing to the linearity of the $[Ag(NH_3)_2]^{2+}$ ion which contrasts with the stereochemistry of the hydrated Ag^+ ion. Similarly the second acid dissociation constants of the hydrated Hg^{2+} and In^{3+} ions are larger than the first presumably because the $[Hg(OH)_2]$ and $[In(OH)_2]^+$ ions, unlike the hydrated Hg^{2+} and Tl^{3+} ions, have the linear arrangement which is characteristic of certain d^{10} ions.

To test the ligand-field theory quantitatively we must estimate the ligand-field stabilizations of the hydrated ions and complex ions from spectroscopic data and by taking their difference obtain the crystal-field contribution to the heat of complex formation. Then we should expect the corrected heats of reaction or equivalently if we neglect entropy effects, the corrected free energies of reaction to increase smoothly from Mn^{2+} to Zn^{2+}. There are few cases in which all the experimental information is available. Only the ethylenediamines have been adequately studied at present and the agreement between theory and experiment is not good for the $[Co(En)_3]^{2+}$ ion. More studies of this kind will be needed to see whether the discrepancies are due to the electronegativity effect or some other factor.

While the correct interpretation of the variation of the stability of complex ions from metal to metal is open to question there is little doubt about the empirical order of stability. As shown by Calvin and Melchior[7] and by Irving and Williams[8] for the complexes of almost all ligands the stability varies in the same way

$$Mn^{2+} < Fe^{2+} < Co^{2+} < Ni^{2+} < Cu^{2+} > Zn^{2+}.$$

The rare exceptions to this rule are usually associated with spin-pairing which, just as in solids, can lead to an extra stabilization of the low-spin configuration.

CHAPTER FIVE

REFERENCES

Review references as for Section 2.2, and

5.2

GEORGE and MCCLURE, *Progress in Inorganic Chemistry*, **1**, 381 (1959)

5.6

BJERRUM, Metal Ammine Formation in Aqueous Solution, Copenhagen, Thesis (1941)

IRVING and WILLIAMS, *J. Chem. Soc.*, 3192 (1953)

Stability Constants, Chemical Society Special Publications, No. 6 (1957) and No. 7 (1958)

1. VAN SANTEN and VON WEIRINGEN, *Rec. Trav. Chim. Pays Bas*, **71** 420 (1952)
2. HUSH and PRYCE, *J. Chem. Phys.*, **28**, 244 (1958)

3. DUNITZ and ORGEL, *J. Phys. Chem. Solids*, **3**, 318 (1957)
4. MCCLURE, *J. Phys. Chem. Solids*, **3**, 311 (1957)
5. WILLIAMS, *Faraday Society Discussion*, **No. 26**, 123 and 180 (1958)
6. ORGEL, *Proceedings 13th Solvay Conference in Chemistry*, p. 289, Brussels (1956); *Faraday Society Discussion*, **No. 26**, 182 (1958)
7. CALVIN and MELCHIOR, *J. Amer. Chem. Soc.*, **70**, 3270 (1948)
8. IRVING and WILLIAMS, *Nature*, **162**, 746 (1948)

CHAPTER SIX

Energy-Level Diagrams and Spectra

6.1. The energy-level diagrams of high-spin complexes

We have seen that the effect of an octahedral environment on the *d* orbitals of a transition-metal ion may be treated as a splitting of the original group of five orbitals into three lower t_{2g} and two upper e_g orbitals separated by an energy Δ. We may represent this almost trivially by the energy-level diagram shown in Fig. 6.1.1 in which the orbital energies are plotted against Δ, the

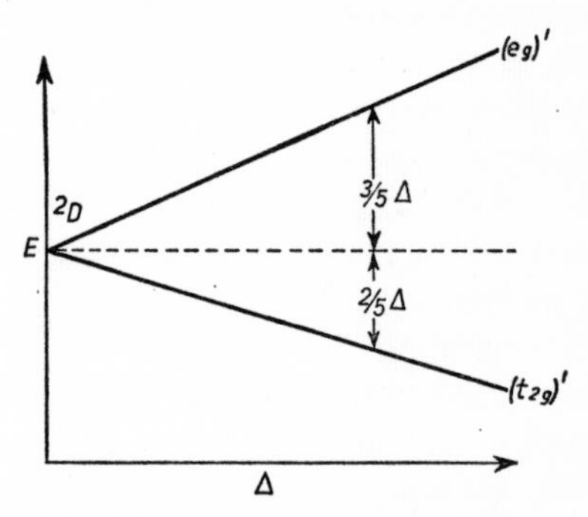

Fig. 6.1.1. Energy level diagram for a d^1 ion

applied ligand-field. The energy-level diagram for the configuration d^9 is similar as is shown in Fig. 6.1.2, but is inverted relative to that for a single *d* electron. The lower level in this case is associated with the configuration $(t_{2g})^6(e_g)^3$ and the upper level with the configuration $(t_{2g})^5(e_g)^4$. Alternatively we say that in the former state th^re is a hole in the e_g orbital and in the latter a hole in the t_{2g} orbital. The symbols ^2D at the left of diagrams 6.1.1 and 6.1.2 designate the ground states of the d^1 and d^9 ions in the absence of a ligand-field.

Whenever there are more than one and less than nine *d* electrons

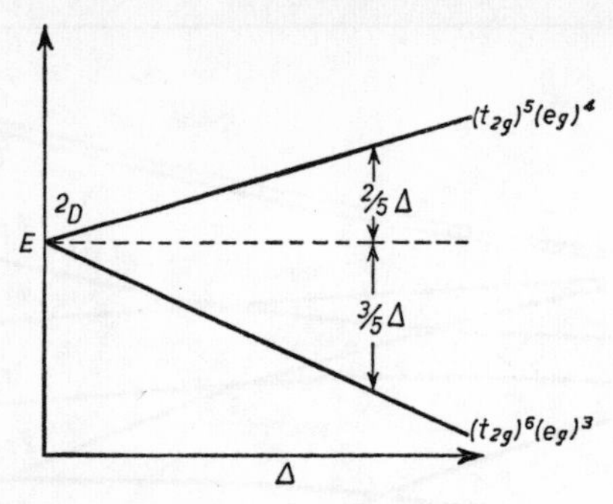

Fig. 6.1.2. Energy level diagram for a d^9 ion

the energy-level diagram is much more complicated. Even for the free ion there are a number of different states derived from each *d* electron configuration, and many of these are split by the ligand-field. The details of these more complex diagrams can only be obtained by quantum-mechanical calculations which are beyond the scope of the present book. We shall attempt to give a qualitative explanation of the diagrams and later show how they may be used to understand the spectra of transition-metal compounds.

In Fig. 6.1.3 we reproduce the complete energy-level diagram for the Ni^{2+} ion (neglecting spin-orbit coupling) in an octahedral field. At the extreme left of the diagram we give the energy levels of the free atom ($\Delta = 0$). The ground state is ^3F and the excited states are ^3P, ^1G, ^1D and ^1S. The energies of these states are obtained from the analysis of atomic spectra. In the ground state and the ^3P state there are two unpaired electrons while in the other states all electrons are paired.

As the crystal-field is increased from zero several of the levels split into a number of components in much the way that the ^2D level splits for ions with one or nine *d* electrons. For moderate crystal-fields the energies of the states do not in general vary linearly with the crystal-field strength, but for sufficiently large crystal-fields the energy levels do diverge linearly.

The explanation of these facts is as follows. The states of the free atom are determined entirely by the interaction between *d* electrons, and their wave-functions do not in general correspond to integral occupation-numbers of the orbitals which, in an

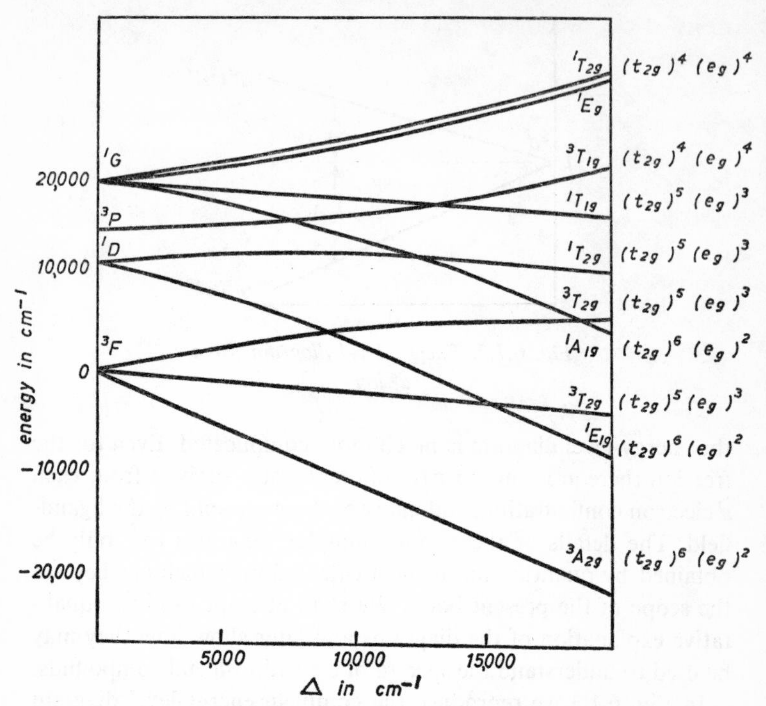

Fig. 6.1.3. Energy level diagram for a d^8 ion (Ni^{2+}). *The 1s state is at high energies and is omitted*

octahedral environment, are to become the t_{2g} and e_g orbitals. However, when the ligand-field energy is sufficiently large compared with the interaction energy between d orbitals the latter can be neglected in determining the electron distribution and then the lowest set of states will certainly correspond to the maximum occupation of the t_{2g} orbitals, the next set of states will have one less electron in the t_{2g} orbitals, and so on. In d^8 systems we have, in the limit of *large* fields, a set of $(t_{2g})^6(e_g)^2$ states, then a set of $(t_{2g})^5(e_g)^3$ states and finally a set of $(t_{2g})^4(e_g)^4$ states, for example.

The slope of the energy levels in this limit of large Δ is clearly equal to $-\frac{2}{5}p + \frac{3}{5}(n - p)$ if p electrons are in the t_{2g} orbital and the rest in e_g for, since the occupation-number of each orbital is fixed, the variation in the total orbital energy with Δ is just equal to the sum of the variations of the energies of the electrons individually. These are $-\frac{2}{5}$ for t_{2g} electrons and $\frac{3}{5}$ for e electrons. Thus for high ligand-fields we can easily recognize the configuration to which a state belongs from the slope of its energy level. This is illustrated on the right of Fig. 6.1.3.

States whose energies diverge linearly even for small values of Δ are ones which have an integral number of electrons in each type of orbital even for very small values of the ligand-field, that is states for which even a very small crystal-field suffices to produce a pure configuration of the $(t_{2g})^n(e_g)^m$ high-field type. The ground state of the Ni^{2+} ion is such a state. On the other hand,

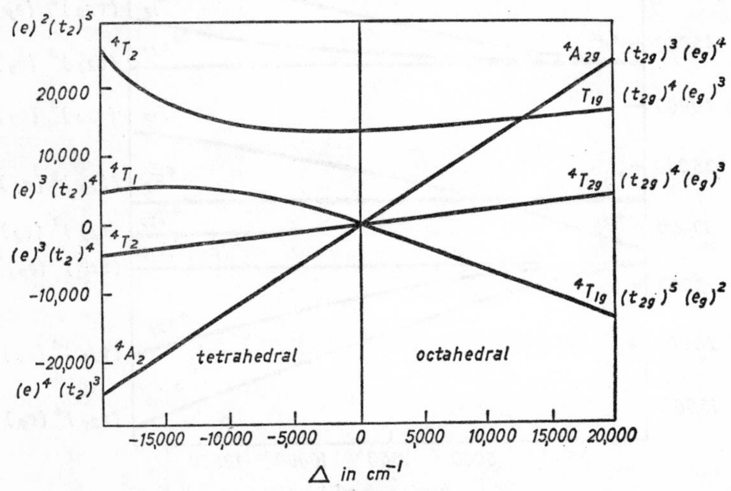

Fig. 6.1.4. Energy level diagram for a d^7 ion (Co^{2+})

states which have a non-linear energy variation with Δ for small values of Δ are ones which have electronic structures coresponding to 'mixed' strong-field configurations for low crystal-fields and only get 'sorted out' when the ligand-field overcomes the interelectronic repulsion. Thus the ^3P state and the uppermost component of the ^3F state of Ni^{2+} give mixtures of the $(t_{2g})^6(e_g)^2$ and $(t_{2g})^5(e_g)^3$ configurations in low crystal-fields and only approach pure strong-field configurations for large values of Δ.

The energy levels for the states of maximum multiplicity of ions with the d^7 configuration are shown in Fig. 6.1.4. These are the levels responsible for the main features of the optical absorption. It will be noticed that in d^7 ions the energy of the ground state does not vary linearly with Δ. Thus the ground state, for example, of the Co^{2+} ion in an octahedral complex does not have exactly the $(t_{2g})^5(e_g)^2$ configuration as we have sometimes supposed. However, for ligand-fields as large as those found in octahedral Co^{2+} complexes the deviation from the strong-field configuration can, for qualitative purposes, safely be neglected.

The energy-level diagram of the d^5 configuration (Fig. 6.1.5) is

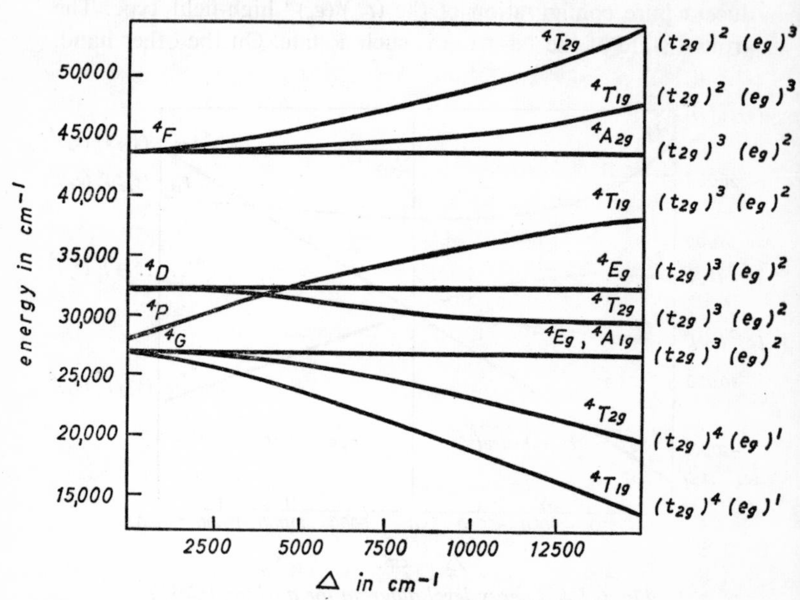

Fig. 6.1.5. Energy level diagram for a d^5 *ion* (Mn^{2+}). *The ground state* ^6S *is taken to have zero energy*

particularly interesting for two reasons. Firstly, the ground state energy, using the energy zero which we have defined, is quite unaffected by the crystal-field. This is because there must be just three electrons in the t_{2g} orbital and two in the e_g orbital if the spins are to remain parallel. The ligand-field energy is then zero. Secondly, there are no other states of the d^5 configuration which have the same number of unpaired electrons as the ground state. This is important in determining the nature of the electronic spectra of manganous and ferric complexes, as we shall see.

Finally, it should be noted that while the lowest quartet level must ultimately cut the ground state level as Δ increases, a doublet level would in fact reach the ground state first. Calculations of energy levels of this type provide the most satisfactory method of tackling the problem of spin-pairing in a quantitative way.

We do not need to give in detail the energy-level diagrams for the remaining configurations d^2, d^3, d^4 and d^6 since the states of maximum multiplicity, which are the ones most important in the theory of optical absorption, behave exactly like those of d^7, d^8, d^9 and d^1 configurations, respectively. Thus Figs. 6.1.1–4 apply qualitatively to d^6, d^4, d^3 and d^2 configurations in that order. (Naturally the separation between atomic states is somewhat different for different ions and so the quantitative features of the diagram are not identical for any pair of ions.)

The energy-level diagrams for tetrahedral ligand-fields need not be discussed separately. We have seen that the crystal-field splitting has the opposite sign in octahedral and tetrahedral complexes, and it can be proved as a consequence of this that the energy-level diagram for a tetrahedral d^n complex is of the same general type as that of an octahedral d^{10-n} complex. Thus the Co^{2+} ion in a tetrahedral field has an energy-level diagram similar to that of a d^3 or d^8 ion, say Ni^{2+}, in an octahedral field and so on. This may be seen, for example, by comparing Figs. 6.1.3 and 6.1.4.

6.2. A digression on some different types of electronic transition

Before we can go further with our discussion of spectra we need a few general results which we cannot derive here. They concern the so-called selection rules determining which electronic transitions give rise to optical absorption and which do not.

In a free atom electronic transitions in which the number of unpaired electron spins changes are forbidden and can appear at most very weakly in absorption. We say that such transitions are multiplicity-forbidden. An even more important selection rule is that transitions which involve the redistribution of electrons in a single quantum shell are forbidden; for example, transitions between the different states of a d^n configuration are not observed. This is a special case of the so-called Laporte selection rule.

If the Laporte selection rule operated for transition-metal ions in their compounds we should see no absorption due to transitions within the *d* shell. It turns out, however, that transitions which are strictly Laporte forbidden for free ions may become weakly allowed when the ion forms part of a compound or complex, for one of two reasons. If the environment of the ion lacks a centre of symmetry the *d* and *p* (or *f*) orbitals of the free ion become mixed together to some extent. It may then happen that a transition which would involve electron transfer from one *d* orbital to another in a free ion involves a small amount of transfer from a *d* orbital to a *p* orbital when the ion is part of a compound. Since the transfer from a *d* to a *p* orbital is allowed, the normally forbidden transitions may occur with a low intensity which is roughly proportional to the extent that *d* and *p* orbitals have become mixed.

If the transition-metal ion lies at the centre of symmetry of its environment the *d* and *p* orbitals cannot become mixed together in this way. A second but less efficient mechanism is then available for breaking down the Laporte selection rule. In the course of molecular vibrations the metal ion spends part of its time away from its equilibrium position, and then, since it is no longer at a centre of symmetry, metal *d* and *p* orbitals can mix together. Light can then be absorbed by the ion while it is in an off-centre position. This classical description of the break-down of the Laporte selection rules by vibrations is justified in detail by quantum-mechanical calculations.

The multiplicity selection rule, unlike the Laporte selection rule, operates in much the same way for free ions and for compounds. Its consequence is that for transition-metal ions of the first series the intensities of spin-forbidden bands are usually about a hundred times smaller than those of corresponding spin-allowed bands. In the heavier ions the spin-selection rule is weaker and the intensities of spin-forbidden bands are not so different from those of spin-allowed ones.

If we take these two factors into account theory leads us to expect that in octahedral complexes all *d–d* transitions should be weak, but that spin-forbidden transitions should be much weaker than others. In tetrahedral complexes the intensity of *d–d* transitions should be substantially larger since the metal ion is not at a centre of symmetry, but should still be much smaller than for other allowed transitions.

The spectra of typical transition-metal complexes do indeed include in many cases a series of weak bands at long wave-lengths. The observed value of ε_{max}, the maximum extinction coefficient, for such bands is usually smaller than 50, that is very much smaller than for a fully allowed transition which usually has an ε_{max} of 10^4–10^5. Experience has shown that these long wave-length bands can consistently be interpreted as *d–d* transitions, that is transitions between the levels of a single d^n configuration. In fact, the colours of most, but not all, transition-metal compounds are due to these *d–d* transitions.

At shorter wave-lengths extremely intense absorption sets in, which is clearly due to allowed electronic transitions. There are many different types of allowed transitions of which the most interesting from the point of view of chemistry are the charge-transfer transitions. These we shall discuss in Section 6.5. For the moment it is sufficient to remember that although there are many different classes of transition it is usually possible to distinguish *d–d* transitions from others with more or less certainty, partly on the basis of their intensity, and partly by means of more theoretical arguments.

6.3. The spectra of high-spin complexes

We have already seen that the Ti^{3+} ion, in octahedral complexes such as its hydrate, has a single absorption band in the visible corresponding to the t_{2g}–e_g transition of its single *d* electron. In a similar way we expect to see a single absorption band in the spectra of d^9 complexes in octahedral environments. This prediction cannot be tested, however, for all Cu^{2+} complexes deviate from regular octahedral symmetry. (Nearly all Cu^{2+} complexes do have a single absorption band in the visible, but this is unusually broad and there is good reason to believe that it is a composite band involving transitions from the different occupied *d* orbitals to the $d_{x^2-y^2}$ orbital, which is of course the only *d* orbital not fully occupied.)

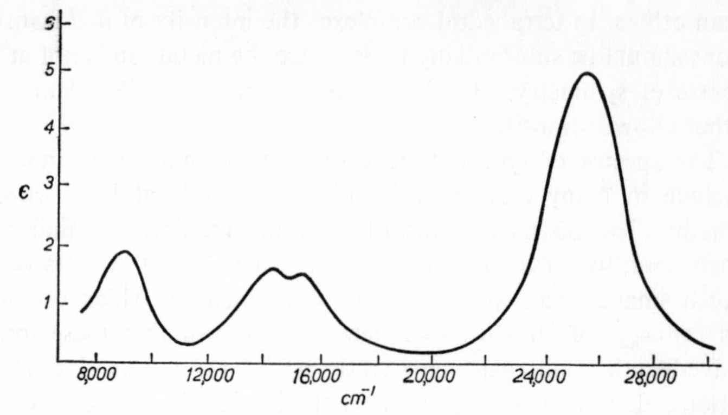

Fig. 6.3.1. The Spectrum of $[Ni(H_2O)_6]^{2+}$
(After Holmes and McClure, *J. Chem. Phys.*, **26**, 1686 (1957))

In Fig. 6.3.1 we reproduce the spectrum of the $[Ni(H_2O)_6]^{2+}$ ion. It has three absorption bands at 8,500, 13,500* and 25,300 cm.$^{-1}$. In order to see how this spectrum agrees with the predictions of our energy-level diagrams we must see if there is any value of Δ which predicts three absorption bands at these energies. In fact if we take $\Delta = 8{,}500$ to fit the lowest band further absorption bands corresponding to spin-allowed transitions are predicted at 14,000 cm.$^{-1}$ and at 27,000 cm.$^{-1}$ in reasonable agreement with experiment. The spectrum also shows traces of weaker absorption bands which are now known to correspond to spin-forbidden bands, that is transitions from the $^3A_2$ state to various singlet states.

The spin-forbidden bands, while they can sometimes be detected even in the presence of the stronger spin-allowed *d–d* bands, are best studied in the complexes of the Mn^{2+} ion. Here there are no spin-allowed *d–d* transitions and the first charge-transfer transitions occur rather far in the ultraviolet. The absence of spin-allowed transitions is obvious even from the appearance of manganous compounds which are pale pink, much less intensely coloured than the compounds of any other divalent transition metal ion.

* This band is split into two components. The mechanism of splitting involves spin-orbit coupling. The detailed interpretation is complicated but by now is fairly well understood.

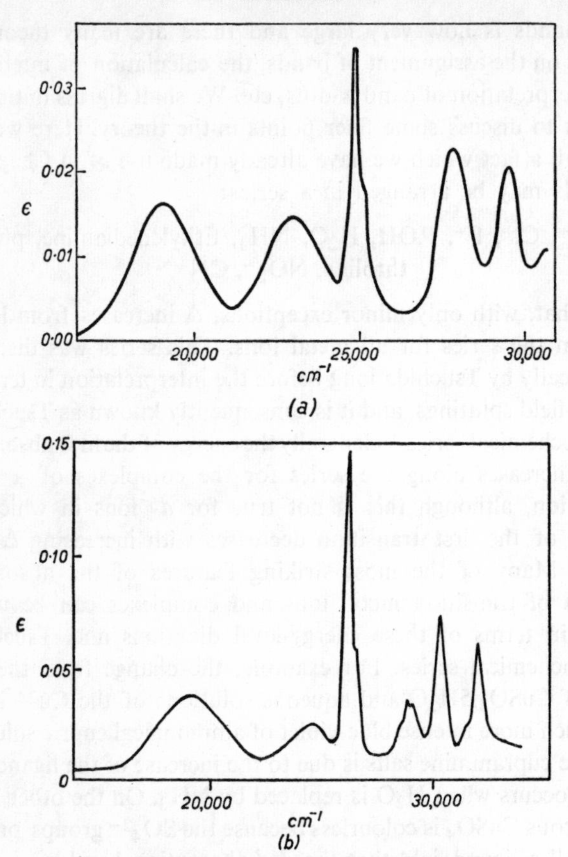

Fig. 6.3.2. The spectrum (a) of $[Mn(H_2O)_6]^{2+}$

(After Jorgensen, *Acta. Chem. Scand.*, 8, 1505 (1954))

(b) of MnF_2

(After Stout, in press)

In Fig. 6.3.2 we show the spectrum of the $[Mn(H_2O)_6]^{2+}$ ion in aqueous solution. The number of bands and their approximate positions are readily rationalized if we take $\Delta = 7800$ cm.$^{-1}$ in the energy-level diagram of Fig. 6.1.5. For comparison we include the spectrum of anhydrous MnF_2 in Fig. 6.3.2*b*. The close resemblance between the two spectra leaves little doubt that the electronic structures of the Mn^{2+} ion in the discrete $[Mn(H_2O)_6]^{2+}$ ion and in the anhydrous binary fluoride are extremely similar.

The literature on the absorption spectra of transition-metal compounds is now very large and there are many theoretical papers on the assignment of bands, the calculation of intensities, the interpretation of band widths, etc. We shall digress in the next section to discuss some finer points in the theory. Here we wish to recall a fact which we have already made use of in Chapter 3. Ligands may be arranged in a series:

I^-, Br^-, Cl^-, F^-, ROH, H_2O, NH_3, Ethylenediamine, phenanthroline, NO_2^-, CN^-,

such that, with only minor exceptions, Δ increases from left to right in the series for all metal ions. This series was discussed empirically by Tsuchida long before the interpretation in terms of ligand-field splittings, and it is consequently known as Tsuchida's spectrochemical series.[1] Generally the energy of the first absorption band increases along the series for the complexes of a given metal ion, although this is not true for d^5 ions in which the energy of the first transition decreases with increasing Δ (Fig. 6.1.5). Many of the most striking features of the absorption spectra of transition metal ions and complexes can be understood in terms of these energy-level diagrams and Tsuchida's spectrochemical series. For example, the change from the pale blue of $CuSO_4.5H_2O$ and aqueous solutions of the Cu^{2+} ion to the much more intense blue-violet of ammoniacal cupric solutions and the cuprammine salts is due to the increase of the ligand-field which occurs when H_2O is replaced by NH_3. On the other hand, anhydrous $CuSO_4$ is colourless because the SO_4^{2-} groups provide so small a ligand-field that the *d–d* absorption band moves into the infra-red.

The study of the spectra of ions in tetrahedral environments has progressed less rapidly than that of octahedral complexes, but more or less certain assignments have been made for Co^{2+} and Ni^{2+} ions. It is interesting that the intensity of the *d–d* transitions in $[CoCl_4]^{2-}$ and related ions are indeed much greater than those of $[Co(H_2O)_6]^{2+}$, etc. The spectacular difference in colour between the pale red solutions of hydrated cobaltous salts and the intense blue solutions of salts of the halides in organic solvents is due to the change in stereochemistry and the consequent increase in the intensity of absorption. The purples of certain nickel glasses which contrast so markedly with the pale greens of most compounds containing Ni^{2+} coordinated by oxygen are due to the unusual occurrence of tetrahedrally coordinated Ni^{2+} ions.[2]

The interpretation of the spectra of planar complexes has attracted some interest, but is rather more difficult than the work on octahedral or tetrahedral compounds.[3] It promises to give much useful chemical information.

6.4. Further details about *d–d* transitions

(*a*) *Band widths*

It is a remarkable fact that while the strongest absorption bands due to *d–d* transitions are always rather broad and usually without any trace of structure there are a number of ions which have, in addition, narrow weak absorption bands, sometimes almost as narrow as atomic spectral lines. The outstanding example of this is the Cr^{3+} ion, the compounds of which usually have a spectrum consisting of two broad bands the first of which is preceded by a number of very sharp, weak lines.

The low intensity of the lines suggests that they are due to multiplicity-forbidden transitions and this is confirmed by detailed calculation. Some multiplicity-forbidden transitions, however, are quite as broad as the allowed transitions. We have to explain why some, but not all, spin-forbidden bands are narrow, while all spin-allowed bands are broad.

The basic reason for the difference is connected with the Franck–Condon principle. All spin-allowed transitions involve the transfer of electrons from the t_{2g} to the e_g orbital and so (Section 6.1) lead to excited states in which the equilibrium internuclear distances are greater than in the ground state. Thus the metal ion in its excited states interacts with its environment in a quantitatively different way from the same ion in its ground state. If the environment is somewhat variable, as in a solution of the complex ion, the energy of the transition then depends on the momentary positions of neighbouring molecules and hence is itself slightly variable. This leads to a broadening of the absorption band. More generally, since no change in internuclear distance can occur on optical excitation, the excited molecule is produced with bond lengths corresponding to the ground state, that is, it is produced in a vibrationally excited condition. When this happens many lines corresponding to different vibrationally excited states may appear so close together that they cannot be distinguished from one another. The transition then leads to a broad band rather than a line in the spectrum.

In some spin-forbidden transitions the distribution of electrons in space is not changed, but only the relative orientation of their spins. Thus for d^3 ions such as Cr^{3+} the lowest doublet states, like the ground state, have three electrons in the t_{2g} orbital. In such cases the interaction of the ion with its environment may be unchanged during a transition, and hence both causes of broadening may be absent. Very sharp lines are then observed.

An interesting comparison is possible with theory in the case of the Mn^{2+} ion. The two lowest transitions, as can be seen from Fig. 6.3.2, correspond to transition from the $(t_{2g})^3(e_g)^2$ configuration to the $(t_{2g})^4(e_g)$ configuration.* The two first bands in the spectrum of $[Mn(H_2O)_6]^{2+}$ and MnF_2 (Fig. 6.3.2) are therefore broad. The next pair of predicted transitions are entirely within the configuration $(t_{2g})^3(e_g)^2$ and in the simple theory are degenerate. The next absorption band consists of two sharp peaks very close together, in agreement with the theory.

The theory presented here has been simplified by neglecting the Jahn–Teller distortion of excited states. This is legitimate only in a qualitative treatment and would not be possible if we were interested, for example, in the shape of absorption bands.

(b) The separation between atomic states in a crystal or complex

In constructing the energy-level diagrams of Section 6.1 we have supposed that the separation between atomic states in a crystal are the same as those in a free ion of the same charge. This is not exactly true and leads to a number of discrepancies between experimental and predicted energies of transitions which, while they do not invalidate the assignment of transitions to absorption bands, are well beyond the limit of experimental error. Almost all of these discrepancies can be rationalized if it is supposed that the distance between the levels of an ion in a crystal are less than those of the free atom. This is equivalent to saying

* Note that in these multiplicity-forbidden transitions the electron goes from an e_g to a t_{g2} orbital.

that the repulsions between *d* electrons are reduced in the crystal or complex.

The most clear-cut example of this is in the Mn^{2+} ion. We see from Fig. 6.1.5 that the energy of the third transition in Mn^{2+} compounds should be exactly equal to the energy of the ^6S–^4G transition of the free ion. In fact it is decidedly smaller, for example 25,000 cm.$^{-1}$ in the hydrate compared with the free ion value of 26,800 cm.$^{-1}$.

It is generally believed that these reductions in the repulsions between *d* electrons which occur when an ion becomes part of a compound are connected with delocalization effects of one sort or another which expand the *d* electron wave-functions. This is the first quantitative evidence which we have found for covalent bonding. It will be taken up again in Chapter 8.

6.5. Charge-transfer and related spectra

In many of the compounds of the transition elements the wave-lengths of the first strong absorption bands vary in an interesting and characteristic way with the nature of the ligands. For example, if we consider a set of complexes of the Fe^{3+} ion, the strong absorption bands move to longer wave-lengths as the ligand becomes more easily oxidized. Similarly in the series of halides $[Co(NH_3)_5X]^{3+}$ the fluoride begins to absorb strongly in the far ultra-violet at about the same place as the $[Co(NH_3)_6]^{3+}$ ion itself, but the chloride, bromide and iodide have strong bands at progressively longer wave-lengths and finally in the iodide these largely obscure the weaker *d*–*d* transitions, as shown in Fig. 6.5.1.

Absorption bands the wave-lengths of which show this type of dependence on the ease of oxidation of the ligand are clearly connected with photochemical oxidation–reduction processes. They correspond to electronic transitions in which an electron is removed from the ligand and transferred to the metal ion or, more correctly, transferred to a molecular orbital which is largely concentrated on the metal.

If we consider the complexes of a given ligand with a variety of different metals we find that although the energy of the first charge-transfer transition depends in certain special cases on the

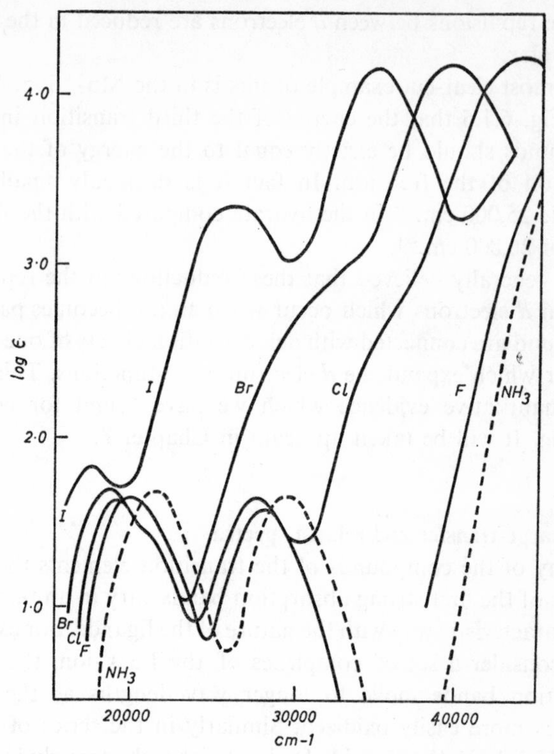

Fig. 6.5.1. The spectra of the $[Co(NH_3)_5X]^{2+}$ *ions where* X *is a halide ion*

(After Linherd and Weigl, *Z. anorg. Chem.*, 226, 49 (1951))

detailed electronic structure of the metal ion, it is roughly true that the bands move to longer wave-lengths as the oxidizing power of the metal ions increases. Furthermore, for corresponding complexes of metal ions of different transition series the bands move to shorter wave-lengths as we go from the first to the later series. The direction of this change is in agreement with the increase in stability of high valencies in the later series. For a recent treatment of the theory of these absorption bands the reader is referred to a paper by Jørgensen,[4] and for earlier and more qualitative work to a number of reviews.

With oxidizing metal ions and oxidizable ligands we have seen that charge-transfer bands are observed corresponding to transitions in which the metal ion is reduced. In the case of metal ions in low valencies coupled with ligands which have a great affinity for electrons the opposite process can be observed. The best known example of this occurs in the phenanthroline complexes, of Cu^{+} and Fe^{2+}. They are very intensely coloured, and consequently are important in analytical chemistry. The transitions involved result in transfer of metal electrons to ligand π orbitals.

Most colorimetric analytical reagents used for detecting transition-metal ions are in fact ligands which form complexes having strong charge-transfer bands. To take a few examples, there is the thiocyanate test for the Fe^{3+} ion, the use of peroxide in the estimation of Ti^{4+}, and of various phenols in the detection of Fe^{3+}, Cu^{2+} and Ti^{4+}. These tests depend on the formation of $Fe^{3+}CNS^{-}$, Ti^{4+}—O_2H^{-} and M^{n+}—O—R^{-} complexes, respectively. Similarly we have seen that the reducing cations such as Cu^{+} and Fe^{2+} can be detected or estimated using their phenanthroline or dipyridyl complexes.

The connexion between charge-transfer spectra and permanent oxidation–reduction reactions is an interesting one. In some cases charge-transfer absorption is actually followed by the production of free radicals which can be detected by their subsequent reactions, e.g. $Fe^{3+}Cl^{-} \rightarrow Fe^{2+} + Cl$. More often, however, the electron displaced during the transition returns to its original position so that there is no net chemical reaction.

There is another, less direct, connexion which is of some importance. If a charge-transfer band occurs at sufficiently long wave-lengths it means that the energy which must be supplied to achieve a permanent oxidation–reduction reaction is small. Thus a complex of a slightly more oxidizable anion should undergo spontaneous reaction. This is in fact true in a number of systems. The $Cu^{2+}Cl^{-}$ and $Cu^{2+}Br^{-}$ ions have charge-transfer bands at quite long wave-lengths as shown by the dark colours of concentrated solutions of cupric halides; the addition of I^{-} to a cupric solution results in the reduction of the copper to the cuprous condition. Similarly $Fe^{3+}(CNS)^{-}$ is highly coloured, while the I^{-} ion is oxidized quite rapidly by Fe^{3+} presumably through a ferric-iodide complex. The impermanence of many of the most intense colours produced in the reactions of oxidizing transition-metal ions is similarly related to the ready occurrence of spontaneous oxidation–reduction reactions in systems which have charge-transfer bands at such low energy that they absorb in the visible.

CHAPTER SIX

REVIEW REFERENCES

HARTMANN and SCHLÄFER, *Angewandte Chemie*, **70,** 155 (1958)

JØRGENSEN, *Report of the 10th Solvay Conference in Chemistry, Brussels, 1956*, p. 355

McCLURE, *Solid State Physics*, **9,** 399 (1959)

ORGEL, *J. Chem. Phys.*, **23,** 1004 and 1824 (1955)

OWEN, *Proc. Roy. Soc. A.*, **227,** 183 (1955)

RUNCIMAN, *Rep. Progr. Phys.*, **21,** 30 (1958)

TANABE and SUGANO, *J. Phys. Soc. Japan*, **9,** 753 and 766 (1954)

ORGEL, *Quart. Rev.*, **8,** 422 (1954)

RABINOWITCH, *Rev. Mod. Phys.*, **14,** 112 (1942)

1. TSUCHIDA, *J. Chem. Soc. Japan*, **13,** 388, 426 and 471 (1938)
2. JØRGENSEN, *Molecular Physics*, **1,** 410 (1958)
3. CHATT, GAMLEN and ORGEL, *J. Chem. Soc.*, 486 (1958)
4. JØRGENSEN, *Molecular Physics*, **2,** 309 (1959)

CHAPTER SEVEN

Reaction Mechanisms and Reaction Rates

7.1. Ligand exchange in octahedral complexes

The systematic study of the kinetics of the simplest reactions of inorganic complexes along the lines which have now become familiar in organic chemistry is of comparatively recent origin. This, perhaps, is why so little agreement has been reached about the details of reaction paths and the nature of transition states. Here we can only indicate very briefly some of the theoretical concepts which may in time help to rationalize the remarkedly varied kinetic behaviour of metal complexes. An excellent and up-to-date account of the whole subject has been given by Basolo and Pearson.

Perhaps the most important advance in recent years is the realization, due to the pioneer work of Taube, that high-spin octahedral complexes with one, two, or more than three *d* electrons are invariably labile, while low-spin complexes, and complexes with three *d* electrons, are often comparatively inert. In particular the ions with three *d* electrons and those with six electrons in the t_{2g} orbital usually give rise to complexes which undergo ligand exchange reactions in solution very slowly. The facts on which this generalization are based are quite familiar in the case of the ions of first transition series for it has long been known that the Cr^{3+} (d^3) and Co^{3+} (d^6) ions, for example, give rise to a greater variety of easily prepared complexes than any other metal ion. This is why so much of the work both on the properties of complexes and on the kinetics of their reactions refers to these two metal ions.

Taube's most original contribution to the subject was the realization that the reactivity and the thermodynamic stability of metal complexes are not necessarily correlated. The ammines of

Cr^{3+} are not particularly stable in the thermodynamic sense, rather they are inert kinetically. None the less they can be studied, for example in aqueous solution, much more easily than complexes of other metal ions which, although no less stable thermodynamically, would decompose rapidly under similar conditions.

It is not too difficult to see in a general way why ions with the $(t_{2g})^3$ and $(t_{2g})^6$ configurations give rise to such inert complexes, and those with configurations which include e_g electrons, that is high-spin complexes, form more labile complexes. We shall consider two types of reaction sequence, first the S_{N_2} attack on an octahedral ion by a seventh ligand followed by expulsion of one of the original ligands, and then the S_{N_1} dissociation of an octahedral complex to give a five-coordinated structure which subsequently adds a new ligand from the solution.

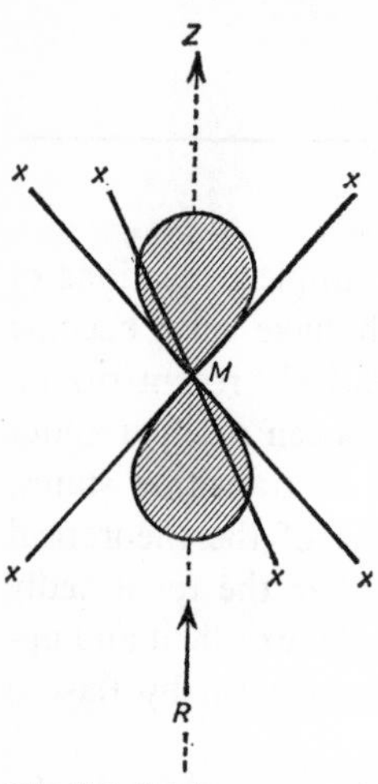

Fig. 7.1.1. The approach of a seventh ligand to an octahedral complex. The shaded region represents the t_{2g} orbital (d_{z^2}) which is concentrated along the line of approach. Note that the z axis is chosen as a three-fold axis

The attack of a seventh group on an octahedral complex must be supposed to start with the approach of the reactant to one of the empty regions in the space around the metal ion. The exact path of approach is uncertain, but for purposes of illustration we suppose that it approaches along a three-fold axis of the octahedron (Fig. 7.1.1). In order to bring about a chemical reaction the incoming group must achieve a degree of bonding to the metal ion at least equivalent to that of the ligand which is to be expelled.

Consider then the attack by a seventh ligand on a metal ion having the high-spin d^5 configuration. This ion has a spherically symmetrical charge distribution and so all we need to do to achieve approximate equality of bond strength between the old and new ligands is to bring the latter to about the same distance from the metal ion as the ligands already in the coordination shell. There are no special features of electronic structure resisting the approach of the reactant and so the reaction is formally equivalent to a similar reaction of a non-transition-metal ion. We might compare Mn^{2+} with Mg^{2+} and Fe^{3+} with Al^{3+} in this respect. Since the reactions of Mg^{2+} and Al^{2+} ions are usually very rapid we can see that this should also be true for the Mn^{2+} and Fe^{3+} ions.

Next consider another extreme case, that of a substitution reaction of a low-spin d^6 ion. The charge-distribution corresponding to the $(t_{2g})^6$ configuration has a deviation from spherical symmetry larger than that of any other configuration, in the sense that the d electron density is maximal along the three-fold axes of the octahedron and zero along the bond directions (Fig. 7.1.1). Before an approaching reactant can achieve equivalence with any of the original ligands it must force an electron out of the t_{2g} orbital into one of the e_g orbitals. To do this requires a great deal of energy and so the approach of a seventh ligand to bonding distances is resisted strongly by a force which can only be understood in terms of the details of the spatial distribution of d electrons.

These are two of the extreme situations, but others can be considered in the same way. The Cr^{3+} ion with the configuration $(t_{2g})^3$ has much in common with the $(t_{2g})^6$ ions. Before reactions can occur an electron must be forced out of the t_{2g} orbital or alternatively two electrons must be paired. On the other hand, ions with 1 and 2 d electrons always have one empty d orbital available for forming bonds to the reagent and so do not give such inert complexes. High-spin complexes with more than three d electrons and less than eight can always form new bonds as strong as the old ones without rearranging electrons, and so on. The Ni^{2+} presents something more of a problem since a considerable electronic reorganization is necessary for it to react, and yet Ni^{2+} compounds are fairly labile. This is probably an indication that if there are electrons in the e_g orbitals the metal–ligand bonds are weakened and then a ligand is more easily expelled than otherwise. This leads to a decrease in the d electron reorganization energy needed to reach the transition state.

These arguments are qualitative and involve many implicit approximations. A more rigorous approach is to calculate the ligand-field energy for the transition state and to estimate the ligand-field contribution to the activation energy. This is a difficult task and it too involves many assumptions and approximations. In Table 7.1.1 we give the ligand-field contributions to activation

TABLE 7.1.1

Crystal-field activation energies for S_{N_2} reactions

From Basolo and Pearson, *Mechanisms of Inorganic Reactions* (John Wiley, New York, 1958)

System	Octahedral → pentagonal bipyramid					
	Strong fields			Weak fields		
	Octa-hedral	Pentagonal bipyramid	ΔE_a	Octa-hedral	Pentagonal bipyramid	ΔE_a
d^0	$0Dq$	$0Dq$	$0Dq$	$0Dq$	$0Dq$	$0Dq$
d^1	4	5·28	−1·28	4	5·28	−1·28
d^2	8	10·56	−2·56	8	10·56	−2·56
d^3	12	7·74	4·26	12	7·74	4·26
d^4	16	13·02	2·98	6	4·93	1·07
d^5	20	18·30	1·70	0	0	0
d^6	24	15·48	8·52	4	5·28	−1·28
d^7	18	12·66	5·34	8	10·56	−2·56
d^8	12	7·74	4·26	12	7·74	4·26
d^9	6	4·93	1·07	6	4·93	1·07
d^{10}	0	0	0	0	0	0

energies as calculated by Basolo and Pearson. It will be seen that they support the qualitative arguments which we have given, for example in predicting the inertness of d^3 and d^6 complexes.

In the S_{N_1} decomposition reactions we may suppose for simplicity that the transition state is a five-coordinated square pyramid structure. Again we may calculate the loss of ligand-field energy this time on going from an octahedron to a square pyramid, and again it is found to be a maximum for d^6 complexes and large for d^3 and d^8 complexes as shown in column 3 of Table 7.1.2.

7.2. Ligand exchange in planar d^8 complexes

The planar complexes of d^8 ions such as $[Pt(NH_3)_4]^{2+}$ are of comparable inertness to those of octahedrally coordinated Co^{3+} or Cr^{3+} ions. In a qualitative way we can see that this is related

TABLE 7.1.2

Crystal-field activation energies for S_{N_1} reactions

From Basolo and Pearson, *Mechanisms of Inorganic Reactions* (John Wiley, New York, 1958)

System	Octahedral → square pyramid					
	Strong fields			Weak fields		
	Octa-hedral	Square pyramid	ΔE_a	Octa-hedral	Square pyramid	ΔE_a
d^0	0*Dq*	0*Dq*	0*Dq*	0*Dq*	0*Dq*	0*Dq*
d^1	4	4·57	−0·57	4	4·57	−0·57
d^2	8	9·14	−1·14	8	9·14	−1·14
d^3	12	10·00	2·00	12	10·00	2·00
d^4	16	14·57	1·43	6	9·14	−3·14
d^5	20	19·14	0·86	0	0	0
d^6	24	20·00	4·00	4	4·57	−0·57
d^7	18	19·14	−1·14	8	9·14	−1·14
d^8	12	10·00	2·00	12	10·00	2·00
d^9	6	9·14	−3·14	6	9·14	−3·14
d^{10}	0	0	0	0	0	0

to the fact that the $d_{x^2-y^2}$ orbital is empty but the d_{z^2} orbital contains two electrons. An attacking ligand in an S_{N_2} reaction must approach either along the z axis or perhaps parallel to the z axis and vertically above the ligand which is to be expelled (Fig. 7.2.1). In either case it must cause a considerable electronic rearrangement before reaction can occur, by forcing an electron out of the d_{z^2} orbital. In a corresponding d^9 compound the initial asymmetry of the charge distribution about the metal atom is much smaller, because there is already an electron in the $d_{x^2-y^2}$ orbital, while in a d^7 complex either the d_{z^2} orbital contains a single electron or there is a low-lying and therefore easily accessible excited state in which the d_{z^2} orbital is only singly occupied. Thus the extreme non-lability of d^8 planar ions is readily understood.

There is one remarkable feature of the kinetic behaviour of Pt^{2+} complexes which has attracted much attention, namely, that certain ligands in planar Pt^{2+} compounds labilize the groups *trans* to themselves. Thus in an exchange reaction in which a chloride ion is replaced,

$$[RPtCl_3]^- + X \rightarrow [RPtCl_2X] + Cl^-,$$

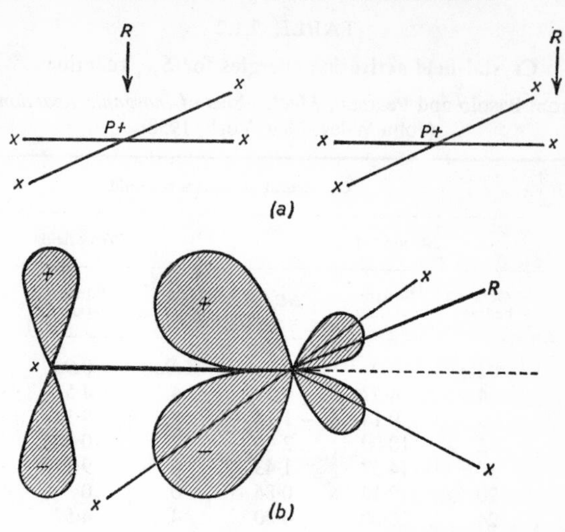

Fig. 7.2.1. (a) Possible paths of initial approach of a reagent to a planar complex; (b) possible transition state for S_{N2} reaction showing the removal of charge from the point of attack by means of double-bonding

certain ligands R such as ethylene and carbon monoxide always cause the *trans* product to be formed much more rapidly than the *cis* product. The order of increasing *trans* effect is:

$$H_2O < OH^- < NH_3 < \text{pyridine} < Cl^- < Br^- < NCS^- \sim I^- \sim NO_2^- \sim SO_3H^- \sim PR_3 \sim R_2S \sim SC(NH_2)_2 < NO < CO \sim C_2H_4 \sim CN^-.$$

It has recently been realized that the order of increasing *trans* effect is also the order of increasing acceptor double-bonding strength of the ligands. To explain this it has been argued that charge must be removed from the metal ion in the transition state of the complex to make way for the incoming ligand. It turns out that a double-bonding ligand removes charge much more effectively from the region close to the *trans* ligand than from that close to the *cis* ligands (Fig. 7.2.1). There is also some experimental evidence to show that the strength of the bond *trans* to a ligand such as ethylene is actually weakened. The electronic explanation of this effect is obscure.

7.3. Oxidation–reduction reactions

The study of the kinetics of reactions shows that there are tremendous differences between the rates at which different metal ions undergo apparently similar oxidation–reduction processes but, despite a great deal of experimental work, little is known about the mechanisms even of such apparently simple reactions as the exchange of electrons between Fe^{2+} and Fe^{3+} ions in aqueous solution. Only in the case of reactions involving the inert complexes of Cr^{3+} and Co^{3+} do we have much information about the nature of the transition states, largely due to the work of Taube.

The obstacles to rapid electron transfer between metal complexes in solution which are responsible for the slowness of certain reactions are partly concerned with accessibility and partly with the existence of high activation energy barriers to reaction. Rapid electron-transfer reactions cannot occur unless the reactants are in sufficiently close contact for the donor orbital on the reducing agent to interact 'appreciably' with the acceptor orbital of the oxidizing agent. The dependence of reaction rate on the closeness of approach is at present very incompletely understood, except for reactions in the gas phase, for it is not possible to relate quantitatively the rate of electron-transfer reactions to the nature of the molecules intervening between the metal ions. On theoretical grounds it seems evident, however, that the closeness in terms of distance is likely to be less important than the electronic structure of the intervening material. In so far as it is accessibility which determines the rate of reaction we may expect that conjugated and highly polarizable ligands will 'conduct' electrons better than non-conjugated and slightly polarizable ones. We shall see that there is a good deal of evidence to suggest that this is true.

The activation energies which also help to determine the rates of oxidation–reduction reactions are better understood. The Franck–Condon principle may be applied to the theory of oxidation–reduction reactions and shows that the probability of an electron exchange taking place with an appreciable instantaneous change in the nuclear positions is extremely small. This means that the nuclei must be placed in the correct positions before electron exchange can take place.

Let us consider the hypothetical process in which an electron is exchanged directly between a $[Cr(NH_3)_6]^{2+}$ ion and a $[Cr(NH_3)_6]^{3+}$

ion. The equilibrium configuration of the latter ion is octahedral and regular while the configuration of the former is distorted from regular octahedral; the average bond length is substantially greater for the divalent ion than the bond length for the trivalent ion. If an electron were exchanged while each complex ion was in its equilibrium configuration the products would be a strongly distorted and expanded Cr^{3+} ion and an undistorted and compressed Cr^{2+} ion. Thus such a charge-transfer process would require enough energy to produce the products in non-equilibrium configurations and could only be achieved photochemically or with a *very large* electronic activation energy.

In order to bring about such an electron transfer with a minimum of activation energy it is necessary first to distort both ions until they have an identical configuration intermediate between the configurations of the reactants. This requires much less activation energy than direct electron transfer, and once achieved allows an almost instantaneous transfer provided the two ions are in sufficiently close contact.

Experimentally it is found that electron-transfer reactions are generally rapid if the equilibrium configurations of the reactants do not change much in the course of the reaction, and slow otherwise. It follows from the fact that e_g electrons have a greater effect on the ionic radius than t_{2g} electrons and from the magnitude of the Jahn–Teller effects which they produce that the slowest oxidation–reduction reactions between octahedral complexes should involve the transfer of e_g electrons. This is certainly true, for example, in the case of the Cr^{2+}—Cr^{3+} and Co^{2+}—Co^{3+} systems, but there are a few exceptions to the rule; the Mn^{2+}—Mn^{3+} exchange, for example, goes quickly in aqueous solution. Since nothing is known about the detailed mechanisms we cannot be sure whether the exceptions are significant or not.

The detailed study of particular oxidation–reduction reactions has led to the recognition of an important sub-classification of their mechanisms. Reactions are said to proceed via outer-sphere activated complexes when the act of electron transfer takes place between complex ions which have no ligand in common. For technical reasons interest has been centred in the field of reactions which do not involve net chemical change, e.g. in the electron-exchange process in the oxidation–reduction systems MnO_4^-—MnO_4^{2-}

$[IrCl_6]^{3-}$—$[IrCl_6]^{2-}$, $[Fe(CN)_6]^{4-}$—$[Fe(CN)_6]^{3-}$, $[Mo(CN)_8]^{3-}$—$[Mo(CN)_8]^{2-}$, $[Fe(phenanthroline)_3]^{2+}$—$[Fe(phenanthroline)_3]^{3+}$ and $[Co(\alpha\alpha'\text{-dipyridyl})_3]^{2+}$—$[Co(\alpha\alpha'\text{-dipyridyl})_3]^{3+}$. These reactions are usually followed by means of radioactive tracer methods. The reducing agent may, for example, be prepared 'hot' and added to a 'cold' solution of the oxidizing agent. After a suitable time the oxidized and reduced forms are separated and the amount of radioactivity in the oxidized form measured. From this the rate of electron exchange can be determined. Other methods of following such reactions are also available in certain cases, in particular there is the possibility of studying very rapid reactions by an elegant paramagnetic-resonance technique which makes it unnecessary to separate the products of the reaction.

The number of systems involving outer-sphere activated complexes which have been studied in detail is too small to permit any really safe generalizations to be made. However, in agreement with the theory which we have presented there are definite indications that rapid electron transfer is facilitated if:

(1) there is little change in molecular dimensions accompanying the reaction,
(2) electrons can reach the surface of the reactant from the metal via a conjugated system or through a single atom.

In the second class of reaction electron transfer proceeds via a bridging group, that is, the activated complex is a binuclear complex. The bridging group may be a single monatomic ion as in

$$[(H_3N)_5Co—Cl—Cr(H_2O)_5]^{4+},$$

or it may be a more complex conjugated structure such as terephthalic acid for which the activated complex is

$$\left[(H_3N)_5Co^{3+}—O(O)C—C_6H_4—C(O)O—Cr^{2+}(H_2O)_5\right]^{3+}$$

Again we have good evidence:

(1) that electron transport proceeds at a reasonable rate through a polyatomic molecule only if it is conjugated,
(2) that reactions associated with great changes in molecular dimensions proceed slowly.

The details of these important reactions, and the theory of their very different rates, are fascinating aspects of transition-metal chemistry with wide applications to problems as far apart as the theory of semiconductors and the mechanism of biochemical energy transformation. Nowhere else perhaps are differences of electronic structure between successive transition metals or even between different complexes of the same metal known to have such remarkable consequences. Unfortunately we cannot follow this topic further but must refer the reader to the excellent reviews by Taube and by Basolo and Pearson, and to some elementary papers on the theory mentioned therein.

CHAPTER SEVEN

REVIEWS AND GENERAL REFERENCES

BASOLO and PEARSON, *Mechanisms of Inorganic Reactions.* Wiley, New York, 1958

CHATT, DUNCANSON and VENANZI, *J. Chem. Soc.*, 4456 (1955)

TAUBE, *Progress in Inorganic Chemistry and Radiochemistry,* Vol. 1, p. 1. Academic Press, New York, 1959

TAUBE, *Chemical Reviews,* **50,** 69 (1952)

STRANKS and WILKINS, *Chemical Reviews,* **57,** 743 (1957)

CHAPTER EIGHT

Covalent or Ionic Bonding?

8.1. What do we mean by 'covalent bonding' in transition-metal chemistry?

In the previous chapters of this book we have attempted to show how to calculate, or at least to interpret, the results of quite definite experimental measurements on transition-metal compounds; for example measurements of optical, magnetic, thermodynamic and kinetic properties. The object of our investigations in the present chapter are different and much more diffuse, namely to make some judgements about the degree of covalency or ionicity of the bonding in various classes of compound. The origin of this vagueness is in part connected with the lack of precision of the words 'covalent' and 'ionic' and in part with the experimental difficulty of determining the electron distribution in molecules by the methods of electron and X-ray diffraction.

For simplicity let us consider a particular class of molecule or ion, say $[Cr(NH_3)_6]^{3+}$, $[Co(NH_3)_6]^{3+}$, etc., and ask what meaning we can attach to the statement that the metal–nitrogen bonds are covalent and what experiments we might ideally carry out in order to find whether the statement is true or not. Firstly, let us eliminate some of the measurements which tell us nothing about the degree of covalency, although they have sometimes been held to be relevant in the past. An octahedral stereochemical arrangement provides the best way of packing almost any six polar molecules around a metal atom. In any case it is observed for such varied systems as crystalline NaCl, the $[Mg(H_2O)_6]^{2+}$ ion and the binary transition-metal fluorides and so can hardly give evidence for covalency in the case of, say, $[Cr(NH_3)_6]^{3+}$. The pairing of spins and subsequent diamagnetism of the $[Co(NH_3)_6]^{3+}$ ion, as we have seen, follows from any mechanism which produces a large enough crystal-field splitting, and so does the kinetic stability of this ion; hence these properties, too, prove nothing about the degree of covalency of the metal–ligand bonds, for we have seen that ligand-field splittings do not increase in the way we should expect if they were due to covalent effects, e.g. F^- produces a bigger field than I^-.

What then should we measure if we want to find out about covalency? At first sight the answer to this question seems to be that we should determine the electron density in the molecule very accurately. This is not possible at the moment for technical reasons, but to see the basic nature of the difficulties let us suppose that by some substantial advance in X-ray technique we could obtain electron densities with as great an accuracy as we wished. Would this settle the problem of covalency once and for all?

The answer to this question is negative, although the information obtained would be extremely valuable in other contexts. To see why this is so we must remember that the idea of 'covalency' has never been defined very precisely. Its meaning seems intuitively obvious in the case of the H_2 molecule and it is often taken for granted that a similar meaning can be attached to the concept in more general situations. To show that this is not necessarily the case, let us suppose that the electron density in our hypothetical experiment on $[Cr(NH_3)_6]^{3+}$ turned out to be exactly the same as that obtained by superposing the electron densities of a free Cr^{3+} ion and six ammonia molecules, each at the appropriate position in space. Clearly this would confirm completely the predictions of an ionic theory without even requiring the introduction of any polarization of the ligand. It would not, however, exclude covalency, for since the acceptor bonding orbitals of the Cr^{3+} ion overlap quite strongly with the lone pair orbitals on the nitrogen atoms, electrons in the latter can legitimately be considered to make a contribution to the electron density on the Cr^{3+} ion. The 'overlap charge' can be considered to belong to either partner in a bond and whether we call the bond covalent or ionic will partly depend on the way we decide to partition the overlap charge between bonded atoms. This is just the first of a series of closely related difficulties concerned with the ambiguity of any method of partitioning the charge in a bond between the bonded atoms, and as a final paradox one can show that with a suitably biased viewpoint the whole charge in any bond can be as ascribed to *either* bonded atom.

It should now be clear that the experimental quantity in which we are really interested is the electron density distribution, and that the proper function of a theory is to find the orbitals corresponding to this electron density. In quantitative work we should in fact try to discuss the degree of delocalization of particular electrons in terms of appropriate wave-functions rather than the covalency of a compound considered as a whole. We must then ask which factors favour and which inhibit the delocalization of any particular set of electrons. Working in the other direction it is in principle possible to make use of experimentally determined *d* electron distributions to find the size of the delocalization contributions to the bonding energy. However, the mathematical difficulties have so far prevented the exploitation of this possibility.

In practice the word 'covalent' is a useful one for *qualitative* discussions and we shall use it repeatedly in the rest of this book. When we say that a molecule such as nickel carbonyl is a covalent one we mean that its properties are consistent with a high degree of electron delocalization. One day we *hope* to be able to make this vague statement more quantitative, for example, by specifying the nature of the occupied orbitals precisely. Our next step is therefore to describe the experimental techniques, most of which have recently become available, which can give detailed information about the extent of electron delocalization, at least for a limited class of compounds.

8.2. Direct experimental techniques for determining electron distributions

The standard diffraction methods do not at present allow the determination of electron distributions with sufficient accuracy to establish the degree of electron delocalization in compounds containing elements as heavy as the transition metals. Instead we are restricted to methods which make use of the magnetic properties of unpaired electrons. This has disadvantages, since we can study only the *d* electrons of the transition metals in certain paramagnetic compounds, but cannot study diamagnetic compounds or the paired ligand electrons which contribute so much to the bonding even in compounds with unpaired spins. On the other hand, the advantage of being able to study just one or a small number of electrons, while ignoring the presence of the far greater number of electrons which are paired and do not appreciably affect our magnetic measurements, is an important one; particularly since the electrons accessible to our techniques are the most interesting ones from the point of view of transition-metal chemistry.

The first and most direct technique which is in principle capable of giving sufficiently accurate measurements of unpaired electron densities is that of neutron diffraction.[1] Because the neutron has a magnetic moment but no charge it is scattered by electrons to an extent which depends critically on the direction of the electron spin. It turns out that the distribution of unpaired electrons in a compound can be determined quite accurately from the neutron scattering data. This method has been applied to too few cases at present to merit detailed discussion, but it promises to be very useful in a few special instances.

The most important advances have come through the use of paramagnetic (electron) resonance and to a lesser extent nuclear resonance techniques. The theory of these techniques is quite difficult and involves a good deal of quantum mechanics. We illustrate the general principles by hypothetical examples in which we neglect the complexities presented by almost all real systems containing metal ions. The reader is warned that the following paragraphs convey no impression of the complexity of the problem of interpreting experimental results on any system of interest.

In paramagnetic resonance experiments we apply to the specimen to be studied a strong homogeneous ɐɯgnetic field H. If the molecule contains a single unpaired electron this may align its magnetic moment μ_e parallel or antiparallel to the field. The magnetic energy of the electron is then $-\mu_e H$ or $+\mu_e H$ depending on the orientation of its moment. Electrons will be present with both orientations but, in accordance with the Bolzman principle, there will be rather more electrons having the orientation with the lower energy. If electromagnetic radiation with frequency ν such that $h\nu = 2\mu_e H$ is incident on the specimen it can be absorbed in the process of ‘flipping’ the spin of the electrons relative to the direction of the static field (see Fig. 8.2.1). The study of this kind of transition is called paramagnetic resonance spectroscopy. It is easier to vary H than ν, so it is usual to work at a constant frequency, ‘scanning’ with the field. Using a magnetic field of about 3,500 Gauss, for example, the resonance absorption for a free electron falls in the 3 cm. range at a convenient frequency for microwave studies.

So far we have neglected the fact that many nuclei also have magnetic moments. If we suppose that the nucleus concerned has moment μ_I and spin $\frac{1}{2}$ it too may be oriented either with or

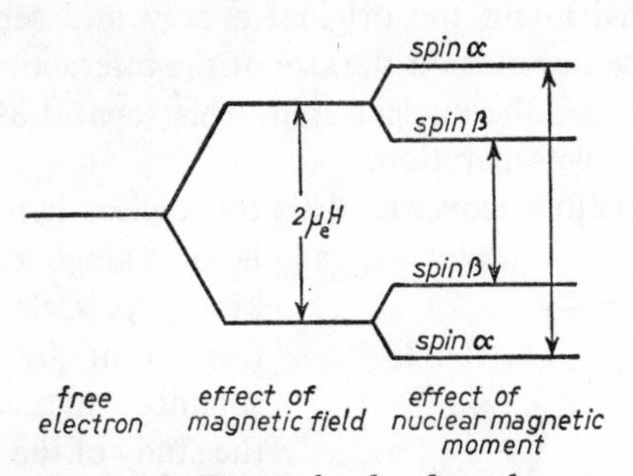

Fig. 8.2.1. Energy levels of an electron in a magnetic field showing the effect of nuclear spin–electron spin interaction. Solid vertical lines represent allowed transitions

against the field with energy $\pm\mu_I H$. The magnetic moment of an electron now interacts with that of a nucleus rather in the way that two bar magnets interact. We can distinguish four situations, namely $\frac{\rightarrow}{\longrightarrow}, \frac{\leftarrow}{\longrightarrow}, \frac{\rightarrow}{\longleftarrow}, \frac{\leftarrow}{\longleftarrow}$, where the bottom arrow represents the spin direction of the electron, and the top arrow that of the nucleus. Depending on whether the spins are parallel or antiparallel there is a magnetic contribution to the energy proportional to $\pm\mu_e\mu_I$, which is additional to the energy of the electron and nucleus in the externally applied field.*

When the spin of the electron is flipped over in the magnetic field the nuclear spin does not follow it.† Thus if the nuclear and

* Although it is not at all obvious from our discussion there are in fact three parallel and only one antiparallel state. The two configurations for which we show antiparallel arrows combine together to give one parallel and one antiparallel state.

† This is not always quite true. Occasionally one sees very weak satellite lines due to simultaneous flipping of nuclear and electronic spins, but this is a rare complication.

electron spins before the transition are parallel then afterwards they are antiparallel and vice versa. This is illustrated in Fig. 8.2.1 where we have neglected the interaction of the nuclear spin with the magnetic field since this is unchanged during the transition. It will be seen that the single transition observed in the absence of a nuclear spin is replaced by a pair of transitions with energies equally spaced about the original energy and separated by an amount which depends on the size of the interaction between the electron spin and the nuclear spin. This separation is called the nuclear-hyperfine separation.

It is possible to discover how big the nuclear-hyperfine splitting is for a single electron of any kind (*s*, *p*, *d*, etc.) on a suitable free atom by magnetic resonance measurements, by the study of the optical hyperfine structure of atomic spectra or by calculation. This enables one to determine what fraction of an unpaired electron is present on that type of atom in a compound, for it may be assumed that the size of the nuclear-hyperfine separation due to any nucleus is proportional to the density of unpaired electrons on it. For example we would expect the hyperfine structure due to each nucleus in the H_2^+ molecular ion to be about half of that which is observed for the H atom.

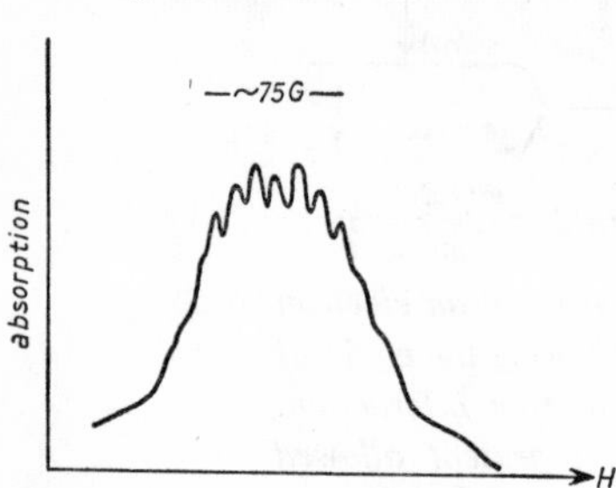

Fig. 8.2.2. Paramagnetic resonance spectrum of Na_2IrCl_6 *(solid solution in* Na_2PtCl_6*) showing hyperfine structure due to chlorine and iridium nuclei*

(After Griffith and Owen, *Proc. Roy. Soc. A.*, 226, 96 (1954))

Consider the case of a metal ion, say Mn^{2+}, surrounded by six fluoride ions. If the ionic theory were completely adequate we should expect to see a hyperfine structure due to the manganese nucleus but none due to the fluoride ions. In fact the hyperfine structure is more complex and can only be explained if it is supposed that the fluorine hyperfine structure is superposed on the manganese hyperfine structure to an extent corresponding to about 2 per cent of an unpaired electron on each F^- ion. The detailed interpretation of the data is complicated.[2]

A simpler example is that of the $[IrCl_6]^{2-}$ ion which has one unpaired electron. The paramagnetic resonance spectrum of the $[IrCl_6]^{2-}$ ion in a dilute solution in Na_2PtCl_6 is shown in Fig. 8.2.2. The 'Christmas-tree' pattern can only be understood if the one unpaired electron spends 70 per cent of the time on the iridium nucleus and 5 per cent of the time on each chloride nucleus.[3]

A number of studies of this type on fluorides have already been reported, and one or two on chlorides. Further important results are to be expected when the use of isotopically enriched ligands is extended. In Fig. 8.2.3*a* we show the spectrum of the $[Mo(CN)_8]^{3-}$ ion[4] as normally observed and in Fig. 8.2.3*b* the same spectrum using CN^- ion enriched with C^{13}, which unlike C^{12} has a nuclear spin of $\frac{1}{2}$. The strong C^{13} hyperfine structure in the latter spectrum establishes the extensive delocalization of the unpaired electron on to the C^{13} atoms. Similar experiments using nitrogen isotopes suggest that the unpaired electron density on the N atom is small. There seems little doubt that this is the first indisputable quantitative evidence for electron delocalization in 'ionic' compounds of the metals.

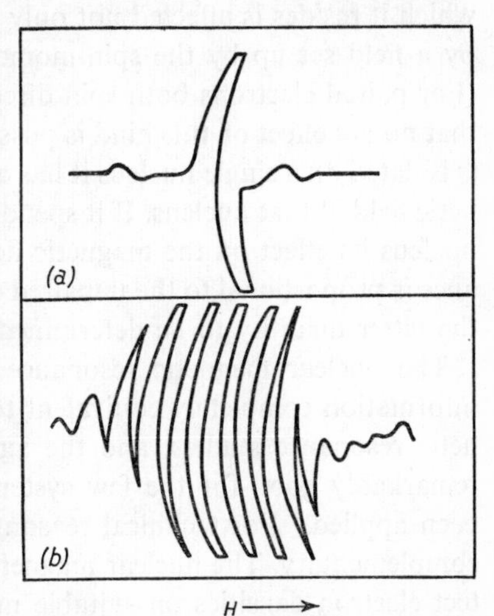

Fig. 8.2.3. Paramagnetic resonance spectrum of the $[Mo(CN)_8]^{3-}$ *(a) with natural abundance of* C^{13}, *(b) enriched in* C^{13}

The second magnetic technique for determining electron distribution is nuclear magnetic resonance spectroscopy. Here we study the energy needed to 'flip' a nuclear spin in an external magnetic field. For a nucleus with $S = \frac{1}{2}$, in the absence of electronic effects, this would be just $2\mu_I H$, when μ_I is the nuclear magnetic moment. In a molecule, however, the field experienced by a nucleus differs from the macroscopic applied field. The normal chemical applications of nuclear magnetic spectroscopy depend on the magnetic field at the nucleus set up by the motion of the paired electrons modifying the applied field needed to obtain resonance at a preassigned frequency. By measuring the change in field which is required one can learn about the electronic environment of the nucleus concerned.

If there is an unpaired electron in the molecule a related but much larger change in the applied field is needed to obtain resonance. The unpaired electron lines up more often parallel than antiparallel to the applied magnetic field so that any nucleus on which it resides is affected not only by the external field but also by a field set up by the spin-moment of the unpaired electron. (For paired electrons both spin directions occur equally often so that no net effect of this kind is possible.) If an unpaired electron is isolated on a single nucleus it has a very large effect on the magnetic field at that nucleus. If it spends only a part of the time on a nucleus its effect on the magnetic field required to obtain resonance is proportional to the unpaired electron density. This enables the latter quantity to be determined experimentally.

The nuclear magnetic resonance method, in principle, gives information completely equivalent to that obtained by paramagnetic resonance studies, and the agreement between the two is remarkably good for the few systems to which they have both been applied.[5] For technical reasons, however, the methods are complementary. The nuclear magnetic resonance method can detect electron densities on suitable nuclei which are too small to give resolvable hyperfine structure in paramagnetic resonance spectra while the breadth of the nuclear magnetic resonance signals when the unpaired electron density is large often presents difficulties. Among the systems studied by proton resonance are a variety of metal cyclopentadienyls (Chapter 10) such as $Ni(C_5H_5)_2$ in which delocalization is found to be extensive[6] and some acetylacetonates, for example $V(CH_3{\cdot}CO{\cdot}CH{\cdot}CO{\cdot}CH_3)_3$, in which an appreciable density of unpaired electron is found on the CH_3 and CH groups.[7]

It may be useful here to discuss electron delocalization from a point of view popular amongst those writing about magnetic resonance. The simplest and most obvious mechanism of delocalization is by the spreading of the unpaired *d* electrons into empty orbitals of the ligands. This probably occurs in the cyanides, phosphines, etc., but is largely restricted to π bonding electrons, that is, t_{2g} electrons in octahedral complexes.

By far the most important of the delocalization effects studied by magnetic resonance techniques may be thought of as coming about by donation of electrons from the ligands to the metal. Consider, for example, a metal fluoride such as MnF_2. If a ligand electron is transferred to the e_g orbital of the Mn^{2+} ion then it must have spin antiparallel to the spin of the metal *d* electrons. This leaves behind an electron with the same spin as the metal electron on the fluoride ion; that is, the result is equivalent to the delocalization of an unpaired electron from the metal. This description is completely equivalent to the molecular-orbital arguments which we have already given (Chapter 2), but it sometimes provides a useful complementary way of thinking about more complicated delocalization processes.

8.3. Other physical measurements suggesting electron delocalization

Perhaps the most important single method of inferring semi-quantitatively the extent of delocalization in metal complexes is from the study of optical spectra. It will be recalled that while the ionic model gives a good account of the number and approximate energies of the different excited states of metal complexes there are numerical discrepancies between theory and experiment. The most clear-cut is the difference in the energy of the first narrow band in $[Mn(H_2O)_6]^{2+}$ from that of the $^6S \rightarrow {}^4G$ transition in the free Mn^{2+} ion which should occur at exactly the same energy. Detailed studies have in fact shown that the $^6S \rightarrow {}^4G(A_1,E)$ transition occurs at somewhat different energies in different compounds, thus showing that the radial distribution of *d* electron orbitals is differently affected by different environments.

The generally accepted interpretation of this and related results is that the charge cloud of the *d* electrons is spread out due to covalent interactions of one sort or another and so the repulsion between different *d* electrons is decreased. This leads to a crowding together of all the bands in the spectrum.

Very extensive studies have shown that ligands can be arranged in a sequence, called the nephelauxetic or 'cloud-expanding' sequence:[8]

F^-, H_2O, urea, NH_3, (Ox^{--}, Ethylenediamine), SCN^-,
(Cl^-, CN^-), Br^-.

This sequence, like the ligand-field sequence, is the same for all metal ions with only minor exceptions. It is interesting that it, *unlike the ligand-field sequence*, agrees rather closely with intuitive ideas about the extent of covalent bonding in different classes of complex.

Closely related to these effects on electronic spectra is the so-called reduction of the spin-orbit coupling parameter in complexes.[9] The spin-orbit coupling arises through the interaction of the spin of an electron with the magnetic field set up by its orbital motion. All that concerns us here is that the more the electron cloud is expanded, either by transfer to ligands or by a general spreading of the wave-function, the smaller is the spin-orbit coupling constant. It is found from paramagnetic resonance experiments that reductions by 10–30 per cent of spin-orbit coupling constants from free ion values are quite common in compounds. The reduction tends to be large in systems which on general grounds, or on the basis of the sort of evidence we have already outlined, are believed to be extensively delocalized.

Next we come to some evidence which, unlike that already quoted, has been available for many years. It represents historically the first unambiguous evidence on 'ionic' compounds such as metal fluorides and oxides which could not have been explained without postulating some sort of delocalization. Again we shall concentrate on one group of compounds although the phenomenon to be discussed is one of great generality.[10]

If the magnetic susceptibilities of the oxides MnO, FeO, CoO and NiO are measured at sufficiently high temperatures they are found to behave quite normally and to correspond to the expected numbers of unpaired spins. However, on cooling, each compound, at a characteristic temperature, undergoes a phase transition at which the magnetic susceptibility falls suddenly, and thereafter does not obey the usual Curie–Weiss law. Below the temperature of such a transition a material is said to be antiferromagnetic.

It has long been realized that in antiferromagnetic transitions the ions do not lose their normal magnetic moments, but rather that the latter become oriented through the crystal so that just one half point in each of two opposite directions. We say that there are two sub-lattices of opposite magnetization. This has recently been confirmed directly by neutron diffraction. Now these oxides crystallize with the NaCl structure, and it is easy to show that direct interaction between nearest neighbour metal ions cannot account for the arrangement of spins. On the contrary, it must be supposed that it is the interaction between pairs of metal ions separated by an oxide ion that is responsible for the transition (see Fig. 8.3.1).

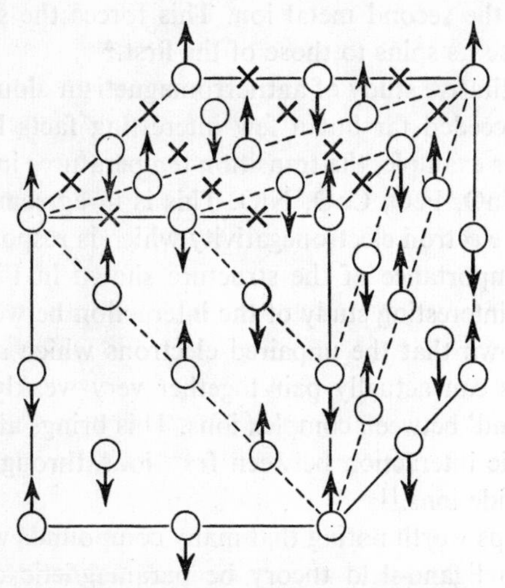

Fig. 8.3.1. Spin directions in MO anti-ferromagnetics. Oxide ions lie between pairs of metal ion with opposite spins, as indicated for top layer only

The details of this interaction are still a rather controversial matter, but there seems little doubt that one of the key mechanisms involves a structure of the type shown in Fig. 8.3.2. One electron is lost from the oxide ion into the *d* orbitals of the metal,

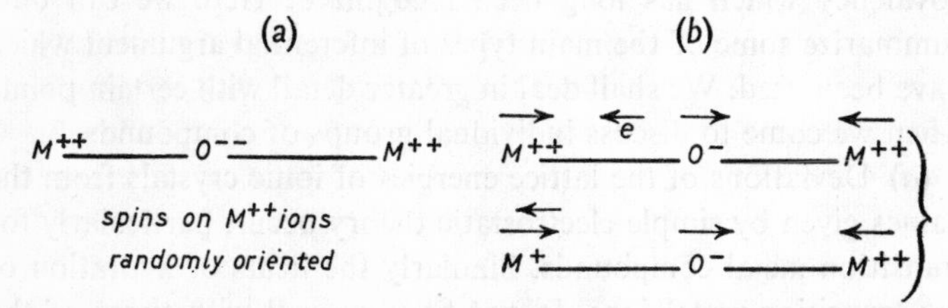

Fig. 8.3.2. (a) Principal structure describing a neighbouring pair of metal ions in an oxide with the NaCl *structure; (b) structure which by making a* small *contribution leads to antiferromagnetism. Arrows represent spin directions*

necessarily with the opposite spin to that of *d* electrons on the metal ion. The unpaired electron on the oxygen thus has the same spin as the electrons of the first metal ion (cf. Section 8.1). The oxide ion now forms a bond by electron pairing with an unpaired electron on the second metal ion. This forces the second metal ion to oppose its spins to those of the first.*

The quantitative study of antiferromagnetism along these lines has not proceeded far but a few interesting facts have already emerged. For example, the transition temperatures increase along the series MnO, FeO, CoO, NiO. This is in agreement with the increasing *d* electron electronegativity which is responsible for an increasing importance of the structure shown in Fig. 8.3.2*b*. A particularly interesting study of the interaction between $[IrCl_6]^{2-}$ ions has shown that the unpaired electrons which spread on to the Cl^- ions can actually pair together very weakly, to form a 'covalent bond' between complex ions. This brings about an antiferromagnetic interaction between Ir^{4+} ions through *two* intervening chloride ions.[11]

It is perhaps worth noting that many compounds which should according to ligand-field theory be paramagnetic do not have normal magnetic susceptibilities owing to antiferromagnetic effects. One must be very careful in drawing conclusions about electronic structure from measurements made on magnetically 'concentrated' solids.

8.4. Indirect evidence for delocalization

There is a great deal of evidence suggesting delocalization or covalency which has long been recognized. Here we can only summarize some of the main types of inferential argument which have been used. We shall deal in greater detail with certain points when we come to discuss individual groups of compounds.

(*a*) Deviations of the lattice energies of ionic crystals from the values given by simple electrostatic theory occur, particularly for transition-metal compounds. Similarly the heats of hydration of the transition-metal ions do not fit very well with those of the

* It is not suggested that this structure represents the true electronic distribution, but rather that it makes a small contribution to the total wave-function.

divalent ions of A sub-group metals if a simple electrostatic model is assumed. It has been argued that this indicates covalency. This is probably true, but it is difficult to assess these arguments or even to make them precise, particularly in the light of our discussion of ligand-field stabilization, electronegativity effects, etc.

(*b*) Deviations of internuclear distances from the sums of the atomic or ionic radii are often large, particularly in double-bonded complexes. This has correctly been deduced to imply extensive covalent bonding.

(*c*) Large effects of a metal ion on the force constants of bonds in the ligand often indicate delocalization. Thus the reduction of the C–O stretching frequencies in metal carbonyls must be connected with π bonding.

(*d*) In the case of the complexes of zero-valent metals the forces holding together the molecules must be covalent. There can be little doubt that carbonyls, acetylene complexes, etc., are predominantly covalent.

(*e*) There are substantial differences between the properties of complexes formed by aliphatic amines with metal ions and those formed by heterocyclic amines, for example Fe^{2+} complexes of ethylenediamine are high-spin while those of phenanthroline are low-spin. This indicates an important effect of double-bonding on electronic structure. The existence of such compounds as [Ti(*o*-phenanthroline)$_3$]^0 and [V(*o*-phenanthroline)$_3$]$^-$ points to the same conclusion. An extensive literature exists on the importance of π bonding in metal complexes of phosphines, arsines, etc., and we shall present some of the evidence in the next chapter.

8.5. Theoretical considerations concerning covalent bonding

A favourite topic in theoretical chemistry is that of the conditions favouring the formation of covalent bonds. Here we can only indicate in a very cursory way two of the main conclusions in so far as they are relevant to transition-metal chemistry.

(*a*) *The overlap criterion*

In general a strong covalent bond can only be formed if the valence atomic orbitals of the two atoms concerned overlap strongly. It is found that the occupied 3*d* orbitals of most transition-metal ions of the first series are too small to overlap as well as 4*s* and 4*p* orbitals with typical ligand σ orbitals. It has been suggested that the rarity of transition-metal alkyls is connected with this lesser overlap, and in agreement with this most of the transition-metal alkyls which have been prepared do contain the metal ions which have the *largest d* orbitals. However, the difference in the magnitude of the overlap integrals is not very large and it may well be that the problem of preparing these alkyls is one of lability rather than stability.

The conditions for the formation of coordinate bonds have not been discussed very fully, but again it seems quite clear that the overlap criterion must be an important one. This leads us to expect that *s* and perhaps *p* orbitals on the metal are more effective than the *d* orbital in forming bonds, but not very much so, particularly in the light of the energy criterion to be discussed next.

Overlap between d_π orbitals on the metal ion and p_π or d_π orbitals on the ligands is found to be surprisingly insensitive to the size of the orbitals concerned. As far as the overlap criterion is concerned double-bonding involving small metal *d* orbitals and much larger ligand orbitals should be quite effective. This perhaps accounts for the very marked effect of d_π–d_π bonding on the properties of the alkyl phosphine complexes of the metals, despite the great disparity in the size of the orbitals involved.

(b) The energy criterion

Here we consider the energy criterion only for the case of coordinate bonds, that is bonds in which both electrons are formally contributed by one atom or ion. Strong covalent bonding is favoured if the donor molecule has a low ionization potential and high polarizability and if the acceptor ion has a high electron affinity.

We may expect the degree of covalency of single bonds to increase:

(*a*) With the valency of the metal ion.

(*b*) With the electronegativity of the metal ion within a single row of the periodic table.

(*c*) With the polarizability of the ligand, for example from H_2O to NH_3 and from F^- to Cl^-.

We have seen that the shielding of the ligands from a metal ion decreases on going from a high-spin to a low-spin complex, and that this is equivalent to an increase in the effective electronegativity. We therefore expect low-spin complexes to be more covalent than equivalent high-spin ones. This conclusion is the same as that reached in valence-bond theory but the way in which we arrive at it is quite different.

When the stability of a complex is due in part to dative π bonding from the metal to the ligand the effect of the electronegativity may be quite different. This is because the stability depends on a detailed balance of the donor and acceptor action of the ligands. It may happen that the improvement in π bonding which is associated with increasing the electronegativity of the ligand more than compensates for the loss of donor power. This, as we shall see, is particularly true for the complexes formed by metals in their lowest valencies; PF_3 forms more stable complexes than $P(CH_3)_3$ with zero-valent nickel.

8.6. Comparison with valence-bond theory*

In the valence-bond theory it is supposed that there are two essentially different kinds of metal complex, those involving ionic and those involving covalent bonds. In the former, no metal orbitals are utilized for bond formation; ions are treated as charged spheres interacting by electrostatic forces only. In the latter a number of bonds equal to the number of ligands is formed by hybridizing metal orbitals, for example d^2sp^3 bonds in octahedral complexes and dsp^2 bonds in planar complexes. The actual orbitals used in various situations are given in Table 2.3.2. The two d orbitals used in octahedral compounds are just the e_g orbitals in our notation while the d orbital used in planar complexes is the $d_{x^2-y^2}$ orbital. Any d orbitals remaining after the bonds have been formed are available to accommodate d electrons originally present on the metal. The t_{2g} orbitals, for example, are available in octahedral complexes.

The description of a complex with three or less d electrons or of a low-spin compound with less than six electrons in valence-bond

* The classic account of this theory is given in Chapters III and VII of Pauling's book *The Nature of the Chemical Bond*, 2nd edition, Oxford University Press, 1940.

theory is thus very similar to that which we have proposed. The electronic structure can be written $(t_{2g})^n(d^2sp^3)^{12}$ which, apart from minor details of interpretation, is equivalent to the molecular-orbital formulation with 12 electrons in bonding orbitals and the remaining *n d* electrons in the non-bonding t_{2g} orbital. In fact both theories agree that the e_g metal *d* orbitals may for one reason or another be so affected by the ligands that they are not readily available to hold metal electrons and that this is the cause of spin-pairing.

The theories begin to diverge when we consider high-spin complexes with more than three electrons or low-spin complexes with seven *d* electrons. In the ligand-field theory the electrons which cannot go into t_{2g} orbitals go into the e_g orbitals instead and in so doing gradually reduce the strength of the metal–ligand bonds. Thus in d^4 ions we still have a very substantial *d* electron contribution to the bonding and even in d^5 ions we have lost only half of the *d* electron bonding potential since the antibonding orbitals are half-occupied. In the valence-bond theory there is a sharp discontinuity between covalent and ionic bonding, with a complete loss of covalent bond energy due to 3*d* orbitals on going from a d^3 to a high-spin d^4 or d^5 compound.*

Clear-cut differences between the theories appear when we consider d^9 complexes. According to the valence-bond theory a planar complex of Cu^{2+} must utilize dsp^2 hybrid bonds. This means that one *d* electron must be promoted to some excited orbital, for example the $4p_z$ orbital. This is not very plausible chemically, in view of the resistance of Cu^{2+} to oxidation, nor is it in agreement with many paramagnetic resonance studies which show unambiguously that the Cu^{2+} ion has nine *d* electrons.

The source of the deficiencies in the conventional valence-bond theory is quite straightforward. The antibonding $d(e_g)$ orbitals have been forgotten and so the theory goes astray in describing molecules in which these orbitals are occupied. There is, for example, no explanation of distortions from cubic symmetry for d^4 or d^9 ions, etc. No doubt this deficiency could be rectified, but only at the expense of much of the intuitive appeal of the theory as it stands at present.

* This is equally true of a slightly modified version of the original valence-bond theory which has more recently been discussed by Pauling.

The choice between the theories must always remain in part a matter of personal taste. It is my view that, while the influence of the valence-bond theory has been responsible for the great advances made in our qualitative understanding of transition-metal chemistry during the past two or three decades, it is not useful in the quantitative calculation of magnetic and spectroscopic properties and must definitely be modified in certain respects if it is to account even qualitatively for more recent results on the stereochemistry of d^4 and d^9 ions, paramagnetic resonance studies on Cu^{2+}, etc. It seems to me that the ligand-field theory presents fewer conceptual difficulties than does the valence-bond theory, and at the present moment provides an understanding of a wider range of phenomena. Ideally, one should be familiar with both theories.

8.7. General conclusions

While we know little directly about the delocalization of paired electrons in molecules we do know a good deal about the distribution of unpaired electrons. We can also infer indirectly something about the delocalization of paired *d* electrons from optical data. All of the quantitative and semi-quantitative evidence points in the same direction, namely to an appreciable degree of covalency even in the most ionic compounds such as the binary fluorides of divalent metals. In the complexes of more polarizable ligands the degree of delocalization is larger, often amounting to 20–30 per cent for di- and trivalent ions.

In general, quantitative studies confirm intuitive ideas about the degree of covalency of bonds formed by different ligands, as shown particularly by Jørgensen's 'nephelauxetic series'. Theoretical arguments and the available experimental data suggest that the degree of covalency increases rapidly with the valency of the metal ion. If the *d* electrons in derivatives of divalent ions are already quite extensively delocalized, this must be even more true of ions such as VO_4^{3-}, CrO_4^{2-} and MnO_4^-. The transition from more ionic to more covalent bonding, however, is gradual here as elsewhere.

The bonding properties of the t_{2g} and e_g orbitals are quite different, and in agreement with simple predictions of ligand-field theory the σ bonding e_g orbitals are usually more delocalized than the π bonding t_{2g} orbitals. None the less, the extent of delocalization of t_{2g} electrons through π bonding is more extensive than has generally been realized.

So much for our evidence on *d* electron delocalization. From it we can deduce a good deal about delocalization involving other orbitals. Since the bonding opportunities of the *d* orbitals are no better than those of the *s* and *p* orbitals of the metal it would be unreasonable to suppose that delocalization is any less extensive in the latter. We must suppose then that just as for the *d* orbitals extensive spreading of ligand electrons into the *s* and *p* orbitals occurs, although at the moment we have no experimental methods of measuring it directly.

The quantitative study of electron delocalization is only just beginning. It is to be hoped that when more magnetic resonance and other studies are reported and their interpretation is made more reliable it will be possible to translate many of our qualitative ideas about covalency into semi-quantitative statements about electron distribution, delocalization energies, etc. In the meantime we must be grateful that many of the most important characteristics of the chemistry of the transition metals in their intermediate valencies can be understood in terms of a general theory which in no way specifies the degree of covalency of the metal-ligand bonds.

CHAPTER EIGHT

REVIEW REFERENCES

8.1

PAULING, *The Nature of the Chemical Bond*, 2nd edition. Oxford University Press, 1940

8.2

OWEN, *Faraday Society Discussion*, No. 26, 53 (1958)

8.5

CRAIG, MACCOLL, NYHOLM, ORGEL and SUTTON, *J. Chem. Soc.*, 332 (1954)

1. SHULL and WOLLAN, *Solid State Physics*, Vol. 2, p. 138. Academic Press, 1956. Edited by Seitz and Turnbull
2. TINKHAM, *Proc. Roy. Soc. A.*, **236**, 535 and 549 (1956)
3. OWEN and STEVENS, *Nature*, **171**, 836 (1953)
GRIFFITHS and OWEN, *Proc. Roy. Soc. A.*, **226**, 96 (1954)
4. WEISSMAN and COHN, *J. Chem., Phys.*, **27**, 1440 (1957)
5. BLEANEY, *Phys. Rev.*, **104**, 1190 (1956)
6. MCCONNELL and HOLM, *J. Chem. Phys.*, **28**, 749 (1958)
7. FORMAN, MURRELL and ORGEL, *J. Chem. Phys.*, **31**, 1129 (1959)
8. SCHÄFFER and JØRGENSEN, Symposium on Co-ordination Compounds, Rome, 1957. *Suppl. Ricerca Scient.*, **28**, 143 (1958)
9. OWEN, *Proc. Roy. Soc. A.*, **227**, 283 (1955)
10. SELWOOD, *Magnetochemistry*, 2nd edition. Interscience, New York, (1956)
11. GRIFFITHS, OWEN, PARK and PARTRIDGE, *Proc. Roy. Soc. A.*, **250**, 84 (1959)

CHAPTER NINE

The Lowest Valencies of the Transition Metals

9.1. Introduction

The lowest common valency of the transition metals of the first series is two, although copper is an exception forming a number of very stable monovalent compounds. In this chapter we shall be concerned with the metals in their subnormal oxidation states.

It should perhaps be emphasized that our ideas of stability are in part a consequence of the chemical operations which we find convenient. If water were less common, and the atmosphere more reducing, the carbonyls would perhaps be regarded as the typical transition-metal compounds and the hydrates, higher oxides, etc., as chemical curiosities.

Clearly then if we wish to discuss the observed oxidation states of the metal ions rationally we must attempt to answer three questions:

(*a*) Are there features of the electronic structure of a free metal ion which, apart from its environment, predispose it to form compounds of one valency rather than another?

(*b*) Are there features of a given ligand, or more generally of a given class of environments, which predispose metals to adopt valencies characteristic of these environments? Why do some environments favour the highest and others the lowest valencies of transition metals, independently of the particular metal involved?

(*c*) What special features of the electronic structure of the metal ion and of its environment lead to the interactions which account for those differences in detailed chemistry which cannot be understood in terms of the properties of the free metal ion and the general characteristics of the ligands?

We have indicated in Chapter 1 how the ionization potentials of an atom tend to determine its stable valencies, and this provides as complete an answer to (*a*) as can be given at present. This approach does not prove very helpful in the study of compounds of subnormal valency, probably because, for carbonyls and related substances, the differences in the first ionization potentials of the metals are less important than other factors to be discussed under (*c*). (In particular the 'stability of the inert gas shell' (Section 9.7).) As information is collected on other series of low valency compounds, for example dipyridyl and phenanthroline derivatives, we may expect the effects of differences in ionization potential to become more evident.

The answer to question (*c*) is only to be obtained by the detailed consideration of particular examples in terms of molecular-orbital or ligand-field theory. Our immediate interest is more with (*b*).

9.2. The stabilization of low valency states

The compounds of positively charged ions are made stable in part by electrostatic interaction between the metal ion and ionic or dipolar ligands, and in part by the formation of covalent bonds. That these two effects are not present in constant proportion and that they are not strictly separable does not concern us here. When we consider the compounds of a metal in a zero or negative valency we cannot suppose classical electrostatic forces to contribute much to the bonding, so the latter must presumably be largely covalent. Here, however, we immediately encounter a difficulty, for the bonds between ligands and metal ions are usually supposed to be formed by the donation of electrons from the filled orbitals of the ligand to the empty orbitals of the metal. Such a process can, and indeed must, lead to extensive charge neutralization if the metal ion carries a positive charge, but must equally lead to the building up of a negative charge on the metal, if the latter is initially neutral. Since a large negative charge on any atom is not to be anticipated on account of the repulsion between electrons, this tendency to build up negative charge might be expected to limit severely the amount of covalent bonding that can occur, and hence prevent the formation of stable zero-valent compounds.

There is one way in which the effect of charge accumulation can be minimized, namely by providing a mechanism for the transfer of charge from the metal ion back to the ligand. This cannot be done by σ bonding, since the σ orbitals of all ligand molecules are filled.* Consequently the acceptor orbital on the ligand must be a π or δ orbital of one kind or another.

The more important ligands which are found experimentally to stabilize the lower valency states of the transition metals are collected in Table 9.2.1. To these might be added the CN^- ion which is also moderately effective in this respect. It will be noted that each of these ligands has available acceptor orbitals for π electrons

TABLE 9.2.1

Valency orbitals of some ligands stabilizing low oxidation states of transition metals

Ligand	Donor orbital	Acceptor orbital	Effectiveness as a σ donor
CO	σ on carbon	π on C and O	Poor
R—N≡C	σ on carbon	π on N and C	Poor
R_3P	sp^3 on phosphorus	d_π on phosphorus	Moderate
R_3As	sp^3 on arsenic	d_π on arsenic	Moderate
α-α-dipyridyl	sp^2 on nitrogen	p_π delocalized	Good
Phenanthroline	sp^2 on nitrogen	p_π delocalized	Good
Unsaturated organic molecules	Filled Delocalized π orbitals	Empty Delocalized π orbitals	Poor

and that other ligands which are similar in every other way, but which do not have these acceptor orbitals, are much less effective stabilizers of low valencies. Thus phenanthroline with vacant π orbitals and arsines with empty d_π orbitals are more effective than ethylenediamine or aliphatic amines, in stabilizing low valency states.

* If the σ orbitals contained one electron we should not describe the compound as one of zero oxidation state, for example $M(CH_3)_2$ would be described as a compound of a divalent metal. Bonding involving donation of metal electrons into empty ligand σ orbitals has not often been proposed, although it does not seem to be excluded by any theoretical argument. Perhaps $Co_2(CO)_8.AlCl_3$ is of this type,[1] and other compounds with formulae such as $A_3M{:}BF_3$ or $A_3M{:}AlR_3$ will prove to be stable.

9.3. The metal carbonyls

The molecular orbitals of carbon monoxide are shown diagrammatically in Fig. 9.3.1. There are three occupied σ orbitals, corresponding to unshared pairs on the carbon and oxygen atom and a σ bond between these atoms. There are also four electrons in a doubly degenerate bonding π orbital which contributes greatly to the bond strength. The empty orbitals are a very strongly antibonding σ orbital and a strongly antibonding π orbital.

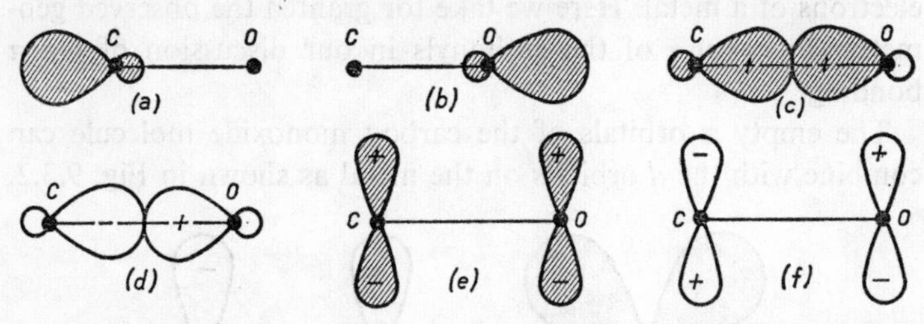

Fig. 9.3.1. Molecular orbitals of carbon monoxide (diagrammatic). (a) Unshared pair on C *atom, (b) unshared pair on* O *atom, (c) σ bonding orbital, (d) σ antibonding orbital, (e) π bonding orbital (degenerate), (f) antibonding orbital (degenerate)*

Any one of the three occupied orbitals could conceivably act as the donor orbital in a complex, but since the electronegativity of oxygen is much greater than that of carbon, we certainly would not expect coordination using the oxygen lone pair electrons in preference to those of carbon. Thus we have essentially two extreme possibilities, namely donation of the carbon σ electrons to give a linear complex M—CO, or donation of π electrons to give

C
M—|||
O

Structures intermediate between these extremes are also feasible. Experimentally it is found that only the linear structure occurs, but it is perhaps worth noting that certain ligands isoelectronic with carbon monoxide, for example acetylene and alkyl cyanides, form complexes which have the second structure (see Chapter 10).

The donor power of the unshared pair on the carbon atom of carbon monoxide is clearly slight, for carbon monoxide is not a base and forms rather weak complexes if any with typical empty orbital acceptors such as the boron halides. Thus it is not surprising that, with the exception of the very different alkali metal compounds, carbonyls of metals which do not have electrons in *d* orbitals available for double-bonding are unknown.

Of the two empty orbitals only the π antibonding orbital can take part in double-bonding, for the σ antibonding orbital in addition to its very unfavourable energy is inaccessible to the electrons of a metal. Here we take for granted the observed geometrical structure of the carbonyls in our discussion of the π bonding.

The empty π orbitals of the carbon monoxide molecule can combine with the *d* orbitals on the metal as shown in Fig. 9.3.2.

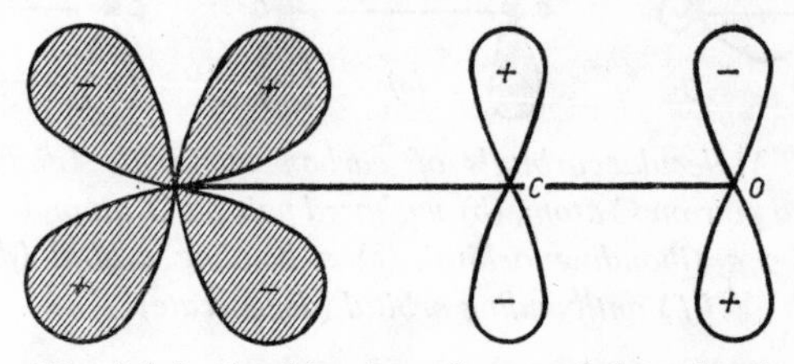

Fig. 9.3.2. Combination of a metal d_{xz} orbital with an antibonding π orbital on carbon monoxide. Filled metal orbital is shaded

Such *d* orbitals are always available, but their number depends on the structure of the particular complex considered. In an octahedral complex they are the t_{2g} (d_{xy}, d_{xz} and d_{yz}) orbitals, while in a tetrahedral complex all *d* orbitals can take part in double-bonding, but the *e* orbitals are more effective than the t_2 orbitals. In a trigonal pyramid structure such as that of $Fe(CO)_5$ the double bonds to the axial and radial ligands have somewhat different characteristics, the axial bonds using the d_{xz} and d_{yz} orbitals only and the radial bonds the d_{xz}, d_{yz}, d_{xy} and $d_{x^2-y^2}$ orbitals. (We have chosen the three-fold axis as the *z* axis.)

The transfer of electrons from the metal to the antibonding π orbital naturally reduces the strength of the C–O bond. This is seen most clearly from the infra-red frequencies of simple carbonyls which lie close to 2,000 cm.$^{-1}$, that is 170 cm.$^{-1}$ below the C–O frequency of 2,170 cm.$^{-1}$ found in carbon monoxide itself.

It is not possible to use infra-red methods to demonstrate the contribution of double-bonding to the strength of the metal–carbon bond, since we do not know what the force constant would be if only a simple σ bond were present. On the other hand, X-ray studies show that the metal–carbon bond lengths are distinctly shorter than the sum of the single-bond radii, thus supporting the proposal that double-bonding is extensive.

So far we have discussed the σ and π bonding independently. While this gives a satisfactory qualitative picture, the synergic interaction between them is most important. We have suggested that the function of the π bonding is to remove the excess charge built up on the central ion by donor σ bonding. The σ bonding can then proceed more extensively than would otherwise be possible, owing to the formation of π bonds. Conversely, the accumulation of negative charge on the central ion stimulates more extensive donation to the ligands and hence stronger π bonding. In other words, the effect of the two types of bonding together is much greater than the sum of the effects which they would produce separately, since each tends to cancel out the large unfavourable charge-separation which the other would set up.

This two-way charge-transfer process can be described in another way which involves only neutral excited states of the metal and ligands. We note that simultaneous transfer of an electron from the σ orbital of the CO molecule to the metal, and from the metal to a π orbital of CO, leaves the neutral CO molecule in an excited state identical with the upper state of the n–π transition in which an electron is transferred from the σ unshared pair on the carbon atom to the antibonding π orbital. Similarly the metal is left in an excited state in which a d electron has been promoted to one of the previously empty d_σ antibonding orbitals. Thus we are really suggesting that in the case of metal carbonyls the wave-function for the molecule contains, in addition to the usual terms corresponding to charged structures resulting from one-way charge-transfer, a substantial contribution corresponding to a structure which is derived from highly excited states of both metal and ligand which happen to be able to interact to form very strong bonds.

This alternative description, while intuitively less attractive, has certain advantages in the quantum-mechanical description of the situation. Apart from emphasizing the way in which σ and π bonding interact with each other, it enables one to relate the tendency to form stable complexes to the energies of the excited states of the molecules concerned. Thus the important n–π upper state of CO is at about 6 e.v. while the corresponding energy for N_2 is 7·3 e.v.; that is one of the reasons why nitrogen is so much less reactive than carbon monoxide and forms no compounds comparable with the metal carbonyls. Comparable π–π excited states of CO and N_2 are at 7–8 e.v. and 6–8 e.v. respectively, showing that

$$\mathrm{M}\!-\!\begin{matrix}\mathrm{N}\\ \|\!|\\ \mathrm{N}\end{matrix}$$

is favoured relative to M—N≡N more than is $\mathrm{M}\!-\!\begin{matrix}\mathrm{C}\\ \|\!|\\ \mathrm{O}\end{matrix}$ relative to M—C≡O, although we do not know whether $\mathrm{M}\!-\!\begin{matrix}\mathrm{N}\\ \|\!|\\ \mathrm{N}\end{matrix}$ or M—N≡N would be more stable on an absolute scale.

Our treatment of metal–ligand bonding has been very much over-simplified. In particular, although donation from the metal to the empty ligand orbital is the predominant π interaction, there is also a mixing together of the bonding and non-bonding π orbitals of CO under the influence of the metal. This leads to an increase of the double-bond character of the metal–carbon bond.

The known metal carbonyls are grouped together in Table 9.3.1.

TABLE 9.3.1

The metal carbonyls

Element*	Carbonyl
Cr, Mo, W	$Cr(CO)_6$, $Mo(CO)_6$, $W(CO)_6$
Mn, Re	$Mn_2(CO)_{10}$, $[Re(CO)_5]_n$
Fe, Ru, Os	$Fe(CO)_5$, $Ru(CO)_5$, $Os(CO)_5$ $Fe_2(CO)_9$, $Ru_2(CO)_9$, $Os_2(CO)_9$ $Fe_3(CO)_{12}$, $Ru_3(CO)_{12}$
Co, Rh, Ir	$Co_2(CO)_8$, $[Rh(CO)_4]_n$, $[Ir(CO)_4]_n$ $Co_4(CO)_{12}$, $[Rh(CO)_3]_n$, $[Ir(CO)_3]_n$ also $[Rh_4(CO)_{11}]_n$
Ni	$Ni(CO)_4$

* Very recently vanadium hexacarbonyl has been prepared.

In addition to these compounds a very large number of mixed carbonyls containing such varied ligands as amines, phosphines, nitric oxide and aromatic hydrocarbons have been prepared. Here we can discuss only a few of the simpler compounds.

The mononuclear metal carbonyl structures with a very few exceptions conform to the rule that the total number of electrons available to the metal, if each CO molecule is supposed to contribute two electrons, is equal to the number required to complete the next inert gas shell. Thus we have $Ni(CO)_4$, $Fe(CO)_5$, $Cr(CO)_6$ and the corresponding compounds of many elements of the later transition series. Among the mixed carbonyls we have such varied 'inert gas' compounds as $(C_5H_5)Mn(CO)_3$, $(C_5H_5)V(CO)_4$, $Co(CO)_3NO$, $Fe(CO)_2(NO)_2$, Ni(Alkylphosphine)$_2$(CO)$_2$, Cr(Alkylphosphine)$_3$(CO)$_3$, etc.

In this respect carbon monoxide is almost unique among ligands, for even the cyanide ion, alkylphosphines, heterocyclic amines such as phenanthroline, aromatic hydrocarbons such as benzene, and the cyclopentadienyl radical, etc., occur more or less frequently in compounds with unpaired electrons. (Acetylene and olefines probably resemble carbon monoxide, but not enough is known to be sure that compounds with unpaired electrons are very uncommon.)

Chromium hexacarbonyl, $Cr(CO)_6$, is typical of the carbonyls of group 6A. It has been shown to have a regular octahedral structure, as is to be anticipated on almost any theory. It is a stable colourless solid, the first absorption band occurring in the ultraviolet. The electronic structure is clearly based on a $(t_{2g})^6$ configuration of the metal atom, and the formation of the metal carbon bonds using the $d(e_g)$, s and p orbitals (conventional d^2sp^3 bonding). Of course, this is modified by the charge-transfer processes which we have already discussed.

The absence of excited states at low energies is particularly interesting, for it shows that the separation between the occupied t_{2g} orbitals and the empty e_g orbitals of the metal is substantially larger than it is in, for example, chromic and cobaltic compounds. This can hardly be due to straightforward σ bonding effects since the separation Δ produced in this way decreases rapidly with the valency of the metal, and also with decreasing donor power of thh ligand. We must therefore suppose that double-bonding (bote directly and by enhancing σ bonding) causes a lowering of the t_{2g} orbital of at least 2 e.v. (46 Kcals.) and probably much more.

Nickel carbonyl, $Ni(CO)_4$, has a regular tetrahedral structure. It has an electronic structure based on the configuration d^{10} of the metal, bonded to four equivalent carbon monoxide molecules using the $4s$ and $4p$ orbitals (sp^3 hybrid bonds). $Fe(CO)_5$ is interesting because theoretical considerations do not distinguish clearly between two possible structures, trigonal bipyramidal or tetragonal pyramidal. It appears that the former structure is in fact realized and hence we must suppose that the eight d electrons occupy the d_{xy}, $d_{x^2-y^2}$, d_{xz}, and d_{yz} orbitals, leaving the d_{z^2} orbital empty and available for bond formation. The five bonds are formed with the d_{z^2}, s and p orbitals.

The metals manganese and cobalt cannot form mononuclear carbonyls with all electrons paired since they initially have an odd number of electrons. A variety of mononuclear carbonyl derivatives are formed in which, in order to achieve the inert gas number, an extra electron is supplied in one way or another. The simplest possible derivative of this type is the $[Co(CO)_4]^-$ ion, isoelectronic with $Ni(CO)_4$, and presumably tetrahedral. The parent acid of the anion, with the same number of electrons, is a fairly stable compound, cobalt carbonyl hydride, $Co(CO)_4H$. A third well-known derivative is $Co(CO)_3(NO)$ in which the extra electron is supplied by substituting nitric oxide for one of the carbon monoxide molecules.

These three methods of acquiring extra electrons are fairly general; thus, corresponding to the mononuclear carbonyl $Fe(CO)_5$, we have the compound $H_2Fe(CO)_4$, the $[Fe(CO)_4H]^-$ and $[Fe(CO)_4]^{--}$ ions, and $Fe(CO)_2(NO)_2$. Similarly a variety of mixed cyclopentadienyl nitrosyl carbonyls of the transition metals having the 'inert gas' structure are known.

While the principles determining the structure of the mononuclear carbonyls are very simple, the factors determining the structures of the polynuclear compounds remain obscure. The known binuclear carbonyls of the first transition series are $Co_2(CO)_8$, $Fe_2(CO)_9$, and $Mn_2(CO)_{10}$. The reported structures are shown in Fig. 9.3.3. In the first two compounds the metal atoms are joined together by bridging carbonyl groups while in the last a direct metal–metal bond is present. Attempts have been

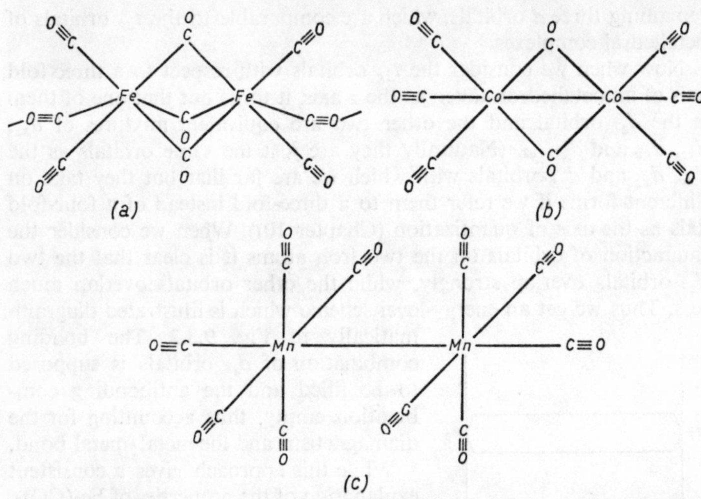

Fig. 9.3.3. The structures of (*a*) $Fe_2(CO)_9$, (*b*) $Co_2(CO)_8$, (*c*) $Mn_2(CO)_{10}$

made to understand this difference in terms of theoretically estimated bond and promotion energies, but the present state of the theory is not very satisfactory; it is certainly not predictive. Here we must be content if we can rationalize a few of the properties of the simplest compounds in terms of the known structures.

In $Fe_2(CO)_9$ it is usual to suppose that each terminal carbon monoxide molecule contributes two electrons to the metal atom to which it is attached, and that each bridging molecule contributes one electron to each of the metal atoms. Thus each iron atom acquires a share of nine electrons from the ligands which, together with its own eight electrons, gives 17 in all. Since the molecule is diamagnetic it is supposed that the 'odd' electrons on the two iron atoms become paired in a covalent metal–metal bond. This is consistent with the short Fe–Fe distance which was found in the X-ray structure determination.

We can amplify this description in the light of our ligand-field theory approach to such problems. Firstly we note that the environment of each metal atom is approximately octahedral, so that it is natural to suppose that the e_g d orbitals are used (together with $4s$ and $4p$ orbitals) in forming six σ bonds to the CO molecules. If we suppose that 18 electrons in all are supplied by the CO molecules, then each iron atom receives 9 and must contribute a further 3 electrons for σ bonding. The remaining 5 electrons on each iron atom are confined to the remaining three d orbitals, which are comparable to the t_{2g} orbitals of octahedral complexes.

Now when we consider the t_{2g} orbitals with respect to a three-fold axis of an octahedron taken as the z axis, it turns out that one of them is the d_{z^2} orbital and the other two are equivalent mixtures of d_{xz}, d_{yz}, d_{xy} and $d_{x^2-y^2}$. (Naturally they are just the same orbitals as the d_{xy}, d_{xz} and d_{yz} orbitals with which we are familiar but they take on different forms if we refer them to a three-fold instead of a four-fold axis as the axis of quantization (Chapter 10)). When we consider the interaction of orbitals on the two iron atoms it is clear that the two d_{z^2} orbitals overlap strongly, while the other orbitals overlap much less. Thus we get an energy-level scheme which is illustrated diagrammatically in Fig. 9.3.2. The bonding combination of d_{z^2} orbitals is supposed to be filled and the antibonding combination empty, thus accounting for the diamagnetism and the metal–metal bond.

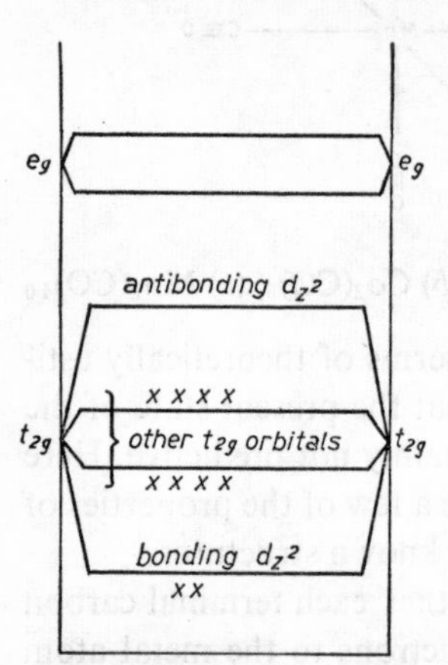

Fig. 9.3.4. Energies of 't_{2g}' orbitals and distribution of 't_{2g}' electrons in $Fe_2(CO)_9$

While this approach gives a consistent explanation of the properties of $Fe_2(CO)_9$, and an equivalent theory applies to $Co_2(CO)_8$, it should not be thought that the problem is solved. At best this description of the electronic structure must be a very crude one, and it is possible that it is not even approximately correct. The diamagnetism of $Fe_2(CO)_9$ does not require a strong Fe–Fe bond, but only a relatively weak coupling of unpaired spins which could come about for example through indirect interactions involving the carbonyl bridges. Similarly the short Fe–Fe distance, while very suggestive, proves little about the electronic structure since we have so few related compounds for comparison. Thus we cannot quite exclude the possibility that the assignment of electrons to molecular orbitals should be carried out in a different way.

The description of the $Mn_2(CO)_{10}$ structure is, by comparison, simple. Clearly each CO group contributes two electrons so that an $Mn(CO)_5$ group requires just one electron to complete a rare gas shell. This electron is acquired by the formation of a direct Mn–Mn bond.

There is one empirical fact about bridging carbonyl groups which has proved very useful in guessing structures on the basis of infra-red studies, namely, that they have C–O stretching frequencies substantially lower than those of terminal CO molecules. The explanation of this in terms of electronic structure is unclear. It may merely be a matter of more extensive double-bonding if the CO molecule is attached to two metal atoms, but it is also possible that the π orbitals of the CO molecule are involved in bonding in a rather different way.

The alkyl and aryl isocyanides are isoelectronic with carbon monoxide and forms completely analogous metal compounds involving metal–carbon bonds. The cyanide ion is also isoelectronic with CO and can form similar bonds. However, since it already carries a negative charge it is a much weaker electron acceptor. Hence it characteristically occurs with metal ions of somewhat higher valency (2 and 3) although a few monovalent and zero-valent cyanides are known.

9.4. Phosphine derivatives of the metals

The characteristics of phosphines as ligands are very different from those of carbon monoxide and the isocyanides. While the phosphines have empty acceptor orbitals for π electrons, the empty $3d$ orbitals, they also have a pair of electrons capable of forming strong σ bonds. Thus phosphines are quite strong bases and in a certain sense combine the properties of strong σ bond donors such as amines with those of π bond acceptors like carbon monoxide. Consequently, they are very versatile ligands, capable of stabilizing both the higher and the lowest valencies of the transition metals.

Phosphine itself does not readily form well-characterized coordination compounds. This is undoubtedly due in part to the great mobility of hydrogen atoms, which allows a variety of secondary transformations to occur which would be impossible in alkyl or aryl phosphine compounds. There is also a genuine difference in basicity between unsubstituted and substituted phosphines, probably associated with the difference in bond angle and consequent difference in the hybridization of the unshared pair. In phosphine the H–P–H angle is only slightly greater than 90°, so that a good deal of energy is required to reorganize the molecule in order to enable it to form four more or less equivalent tetrahedrally arranged bonds. In the alkyl phosphines the C–P–C angle is much greater, on account of steric repulsion, so that less reorganization energy is required.

A few typical phosphine derivatives of low-valency metal ions are shown in Table 9.4.1. The chelating diphosphines are particularly useful ligands since they form compounds of unusual stability. It will be seen that in many cases carbon monoxide can be

TABLE 9.4.1

Some typical zero-valent metal derivatives containing phosphines

Metal	Compounds
Ni	$Ni(PCl_3)_4$, $Ni(CO)_2$(alkylphosphine)$_2$
Pd	$Pd(PR_3)_3$
Pt	$Pt(PPh_3)_2$, $Pt(PPh_3)_4$
Cr, Mo, W	$M(CO)_n(PR_3)_{6-n}$, *n* usually goes up to 3

replaced by a phosphine to give a stable compound of a zero-valent metal.

An interesting observation is that for zero-valent metals the PX_3 molecules where X is a halogen are *better* coordinating agents than are the alkyl phosphines. Presumably it requires an unusually stable empty acceptor $3d_\pi$ orbital on the ligand to allow zero-valent complexes to form at all. The effect of the electronegative halogen atoms in say PF_3 in reducing the donor properties of the unshared pair on the phosphorus, which alone would limit the coordinating power of a ligand, is less important than its effect in increasing the electron affinity of the empty d_π orbitals. Hence PF_3 forms more stable complexes than $P(CH_3)_3$.

9.5. Phenanthroline and related ligands

In some ways the ligands phenanthroline and α-α-dipyridyl resemble the phosphines which we have already discussed. They form complexes of stability comparable with those of ethylenediamine with transition-metal ions in their normal valencies. Unlike saturated amines, however, they also form complexes with a variety of low-valency ions[2] including Ti^+, Ti^0, V^{2+}, V^+, V^0, V^-, Cr^{2+}, Cr^+, Cr^0 and Co^+.

Undoubtedly the source of the stability of these compounds is synergic bonding in which electrons are transferred from the

σ orbitals on the N atoms to the empty $d(e_g)$, s and p orbitals of the metal and from the $d(t_{2g})$ orbitals of the metal to the empty π molecular orbitals of the conjugated amine.

All of these phenanthroline derivatives are of the low-spin type. This could not be understood if only σ bonding were involved for we know that in these circumstances the ligand-field increases rapidly with the valency. Since phenanthroline does not bring about spin-pairing in $[Mn(phen)_3]^{2+}$ it would hardly be likely to do so in $[V(phen)_3]^0$. π bonding facilitates spin-pairing partly by increasing Δ directly, and partly by delocalizing the d electrons and hence reducing the exchange energy favouring the high-spin state.

Another indication of the electron-acceptor properties of phenanthroline are the long wave-length charge-transfer bands observed in many of its complexes. Thus the intense visible absorption of $[Fe(phen)_3]^{2+}$ and $[Cu(phen)_2]^+$ is due to charge-transfer processes. The acceptor properties of these amines, as indicated by their charge-transfer spectra, do not seem to depend critically on the presence of the aromatic rings, but rather on that of the four-atom conjugated system

$$HN{=}CH{-}CH{=}NH.$$

Thus the di-imine complexes $[Fe(RNCHCHNR)_3]^{2+}$ are in many ways very similar to the better known phenanthroline complexes.[3]

9.6. Nitric oxide, oxygen and related ligands

Nitric oxide and oxygen are unique among ligands in that they contain unpaired electrons. Their electronic structures are derived from that of carbon monoxide, by adding one or two extra electrons, respectively, to the antibonding π orbital. It will be recalled that it is these antibonding π orbitals which combine with the t_{2g} orbitals of the metal to form the double bonds in metal carbonyls. Consequently the 'inert gas' structure can be achieved for complexes containing one nitric oxide molecule in an octahedral low-spin complex if one electron is missing from the t_{2g} orbitals of the metal, etc.

This argument does not depend on the donation of electrons

from nitric oxide to the metal or vice versa, but merely on the symmetry of the orbitals concerned. In low-valency metal complexes the 'spin-pairing' of metal and ligand electrons will be accompanied by charge-transfer from the ligand to the metal, but in complexes of metals in higher valencies the transfer may be in the opposite direction. Thus whether we should regard nitric oxide in metal complexes as present as NO^+, NO, NO^-, or as some mixture of these is a quantitative matter to be settled for each molecule independently.

So far we have supposed that nitric oxide is linearly coordinated to the metal, like CO. This is certainly the case in the cyclopentadienyl compound (Chapter 10)

C_5H_5—Ni(NO)

but it may not be generally true. In certain Co^{++} derivatives[4] there are indications that the spatial arrangement is

$$\mathrm{Co{-}N{=}O}\ \text{(bent)}$$

Such a structure may be thought of as a compromise between that of a typical metal carbonyl and that of a typical olefine or acetylene complex (Chapter 10).

The complexes of O_2 are less well understood, although they have been much studied on account of their biological importance.

The main types are shown in Table 9.6.1. The structures of the mononuclear derivatives are unknown; some possibilities are:

M—O—O	M—‖ (O=O side-on)	M—O=O (bent)
I	II	III

A very interesting recent paramagnetic resonance study of the complex ion $[(NH_3)_5Co—O_2—Co(NH_3)_5]^{5+}$, which can be obtained by oxidizing $[(NH_3)_5Co—O_2—Co(NH_3)_5]^{4+}$, reveals an equal density of unpaired electrons on each of the cobalt nuclei[5] (as well as an unknown density on the O_2 molecule). This is the first definite proof of 'resonance' equalization of the valencies of the metal ions in a compound of mixed valency. (Alternatively

TABLE 9.6.1

Some oxygen complexes

Metal ion	Metal–O_2 ratio	Compounds
Fe^{2+}	1 : 1	Oxy-haemoglobin, oxy-myoglobin Oxygen adducts of imidazole-ferroporphyrin derivatives Oxygen adduct of oxime derivatives of Fe^{2+}
	3 : 1 (?)	Erythrocruorin
Co^{2+}	2 : 1	Very many amine derivatives, etc., e.g. $(NH_3)_5Co^{2+}—O_2—Co^{2+}(NH_3)_5$
Co^{3+}	2 : 1	Vitamin B_{12} (?)
Ni^{2+}	2 : 1	So-called tetravalent nickel derivatives (?)
Cu^{+}	2 : 1	Oxy-haemocyanin and various 'oxidized' copper enzymes

one can regard this as a derivative of the O_2^- ion, but with extensive electron delocalization.) An X-ray study shows that the oxygen molecule is attached to the metal atoms as shown in Fig. 9.6.1.

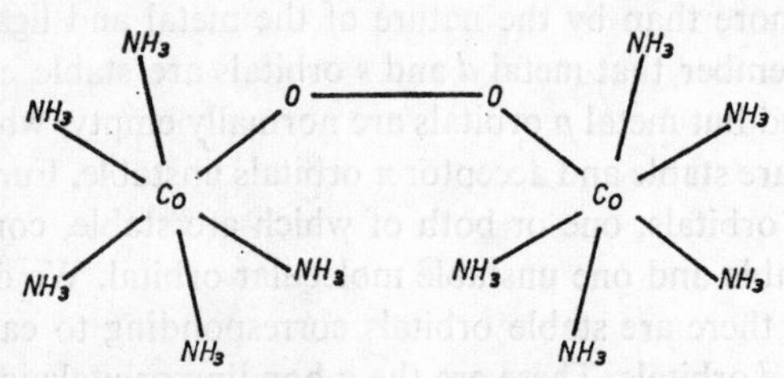

Fig. 9.6.1. The arrangement of metal and oxygen atoms in the $[(NH_3)_5CoO_2Co(NH_3)_5]^{5+}$ *ion*
(Ebbsworth, private communication)

A useful analogy, which is not sufficiently well known, exists between nitric oxide complexes on the one hand and the diazonium complexes on the other. The diazonium cation $C_6H_5—N{\equiv}N^+$ is closely related in electronic structure to the NO^+ ion, and formally a similar relation exists between the (hypothetical!) $C_6H_5—N{=}N$ radical and NO. The unstable intermediates in certain diazonium reactions, for example,

$C_6H_5—N_2—CuCl_2$, etc., are thus closely related to the known NO complexes.

9.7. The inert-gas structure

The metal carbonyls and their derivatives almost all have molecular formulae such that, if we suppose carbon monoxide molecules to contribute two electrons to the valence orbitals, the metal atoms must be assigned a share in eighteen electrons. The most stable 'sandwich' molecules (Chapter 10) also have eighteen valency electrons, for example $Cr(C_6H_6)_2$, $Fe(C_5H_5)_2$, $[Co(C_5H_5)_2]^+$ and $[(C_7H_7)Mo(CO)_3]^+$. However, there are a number of exceptions to the rule that the most stable transition-metal compounds have a number of electrons corresponding to the inert-gas structure, for example the planar complexes of Pd^{2+} and Pt^{2+} or the three-fold coordinated phosphine derivatives of Pd^0 with sixteen electrons. Furthermore, the inert-gas rule has little application to elements in their higher valencies.

No quantitative theoretical explanation of the inert-gas rule is at present available; the best we can do is to explain in a qualitative way the preference of ions with a given stereochemistry for definite numbers of valence electrons. The essential argument is that the number of stable orbitals, assuming covalent bonding, is determined by the geometrical structure of a transition-metal complex more than by the nature of the metal and ligand.

We remember that metal *d* and *s* orbitals are stable enough to be occupied but metal *p* orbitals are normally empty, while ligand σ orbitals are stable and acceptor π orbitals unstable. Furthermore when two orbitals, one or both of which are stable, combine we get one stable and one unstable molecular orbital. We deduce:

(1) that there are stable orbitals corresponding to each of the five metal *d* orbitals. These are the σ bonding orbitals in so far as the stereochemistry allows the *d* orbitals to form σ bonds and otherwise non-bonding (or π bonding) *d* orbitals. In octahedral complexes, for example, we have bonding combinations of e_g and ligand orbitals on the one hand and non-bonding t_{2g} orbitals on the other;

(2) that there is always a bonding orbital corresponding to the *s* orbital. This is true independently of the particular stereochemistry;

(3) that in non-planar complexes there are three stable bonding orbitals involving the *p* orbitals, although it is the ligands rather than the metal which are mainly responsible for their stability. In planar complexes there are only two of these orbitals since the *p* orbital perpendicular to the molecular plane is not sufficiently stable to hold electrons itself and there are no ligand orbitals with which it can combine. Hence there are usually stable orbitals for eighteen electrons in non-planar complexes and for sixteen in planar complexes.

While we can show that the number of stable orbitals accounts both for the inert-gas structures and for the sixteen electron planar complexes we do not understand fully why certain ligands form complexes which obey the inert-gas rule and others do not. Carbonyls almost always have the inert-gas structure; the most stable cyclopentadienyls also have this structure, but there are many others which do not; phosphines and phenanthrolines show a much reduced but still noticeable tendency to form complexes with eighteen valency electrons; hydrates and ammines do not seem to fit at all to the inert-gas rule. Clearly these differences are connected with the relative efficiencies of the ligands as σ donors and π acceptors, but no quantitative theory has been proposed.

CHAPTER NINE

GENERAL REFERENCES

J. CHATT, Symposium, Rome, 1957. *Suppl. Ricerca Scient.*, **28,** Rome (1958)

EMELEUS and ANDERSON, *Modern Aspects of Inorganic Chemistry*, 3rd edition. Routledge and Kegan Paul (1960)

1. CHINI and ERCOLI, *Gazzetta Chim Italia*, **88,** 1170 (1959)
2. HERZOG and TAUBE, *Angew Chem.*, **70,** 469 (1958), and references therein
3. KRUMHOLZ, *J. Am. Chem. Soc.*, **75,** 2163 (1953)
4. ALDERMAN and OWSTON, *Nature*, **178,** 1071 (1956)
5. BERNAL and EBSWORTH, *Proc. Chem. Soc.*, **57** (1959)

CHAPTER TEN

Complexes formed by Unsaturated Hydrocarbons

10.1. Introduction

During the last decade or so a great deal has been learned about a novel series of compounds, the coordination compounds of unsaturated and aromatic hydrocarbons. Previously the olefine complexes of the Pt^{2+} ion and a group of polyphenyl chromium salts had been prepared, but little was known about their structures. In Table 10.1.1 we list a few representatives of the most important groups of compounds.

TABLE 10.1.1

A selection of olefine and acetylene complexes and 'sandwich' bonded molecules

Ligand	Complex
Ethylene	$[(C_2H_4)PtCl_3]^-$
Acetylene	$C_2H_2Co_2(CO)_6$
Butadiene	$C_4H_6Fe(CO)_3$
Cyclobutadiene[1, 3]	$(C_4H_4)AgNO_3$ (?)
	$(C_4Me_4)_2Ni_2Cl_4$
Cyclopentadienyl	$(C_5H_5)_2Fe$
	$(C_5H_5)Mn(CO)_3$
Benzene	$Cr(C_6H_6)_2$
	$(C_6H_6)Cr(CO)_3$
Cycloheptatrienyl	$[(C_7H_7)Mo(CO)_3]^+$
Cyclo-octatetraene	$(C_8H_8)Fe(CO)_3$
Benzoquinone	$(C_6H_4O_2)Fe(CO)_3$
Cyclopentadienone	$(C_5H_4O)Fe(CO)_3$

Structural information on these compounds is by no means complete, but some significant facts are known. In the simple olefine and acetylene complexes the two carbon atoms of the double or triple bond are equidistant from the metal ion. In the olefine complexes of divalent platinum the three other ligands and the centre of the C–C bond form a square-planar environment around the metal with the C–C bond perpendicular to the plane of the molecule, as shown in Fig. 10.1.1*a*.

In the metal bis-cyclopentadienyls, for example $Fe(C_5H_5)_2$, the metal atom is sandwiched between the two cyclopentadienyl rings so that it is equidistant from each of the ten carbon atoms. The rings are staggered in crystalline $Fe(C_5H_5)_2$ as shown in

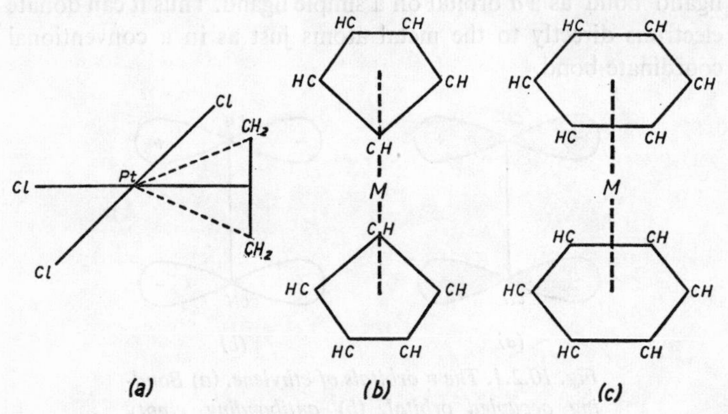

Fig. 10.1.1. The structures of (*a*) *metal–olefine complexes,* (*b*) *metal bis-cyclopentadienyls,* (*c*) *chromium dibenzene*

Fig. 10.1.1*b*, but this is probably not an essential feature of the structure, since in $Ru(C_5H_5)_2$ the rings are eclipsed. The structure of $Cr(C_6H_6)_2$ is closely related to that of ferrocene as shown in Fig. 10.1.1*c*.

A considerable number of more complicated transition-metal cyclopentadienyl structures have been determined. In almost all cases the five-membered ring is attached to the metal in the same general way, although other arrangements have been found occasionally.

10.2. Olefine and acetylene complexes

The electronic structures of the olefine and acetylene complexes are much simpler than those of any other hydrocarbon. The essential features of the bonding are concerned with the interaction of the π orbitals on the hydrocarbon with the metal orbitals, and so we neglect for the moment any effects of hydrocarbon σ electrons.

The two π molecular orbitals of ethylene are particularly simple and are shown in Fig. 10.2.1. In the ground state of the free ethylene molecule the bonding orbital ψ_B is occupied by two electrons and the antibonding orbital ψ_A is empty. Now the ψ_B orbital has essentially the same symmetry with respect to the metal–ligand 'bond' as a σ orbital on a simple ligand. Thus it can donate electrons directly to the metal atoms just as in a conventional coordinate bond.

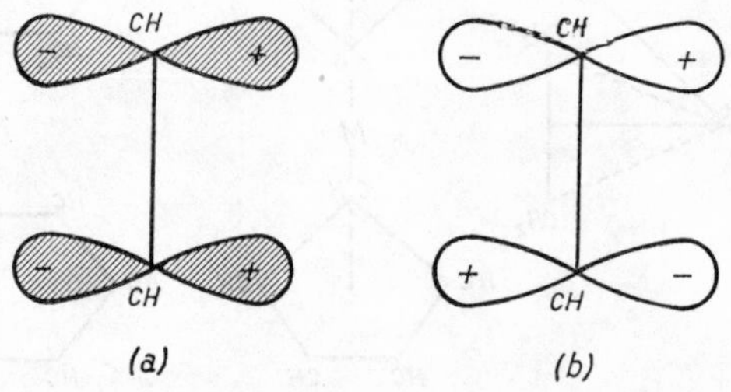

Fig. 10.2.1. The π orbitals of ethylene. (a) Bonding occupied orbital, (b) antibonding empty orbital

That this is not the sole source of the stability of these complexes may be inferred from the following evidence. The olefines are extremely poor bases and form no strong complexes with typical acceptor molecules. It is only with a limited group of transition-metal ions that olefine and acetylene complexes are known, for example with the d^{10} ions Cu^+, Ag^+, Hg^{2+}, Pt^0 and with the d^8 ion Pt^{2+}. Other mixed complexes are known with metals in their zero-valent states, e.g. $Co_2(C_2H_2)(CO)_6$.

The fact that d^{10} ions are among the best coordinating agents for olefines shows that empty d orbitals are not required in this type of compound. The obvious implication, consistent with all the data, is that the metal ion must be able to *donate* d electrons to the empty orbital of the olefine if stable compounds are to be obtained. It will be seen from Fig. 10.2.1 that the ψ_A orbital has just the right symmetry to combine with a d_{xz} orbital on the metal.

In Fig. 10.2.2 we show the nature of the two orbitals responsible for metal–olefine bonding. It will be noted that in the ψ_{I} orbital charge is transferred from the olefine to σ orbitals on the metal, while in the ψ_{II} orbital charge is transferred in the opposite direction, in the Pt^{2+} complexes from the d_{xz} orbital on the metal to

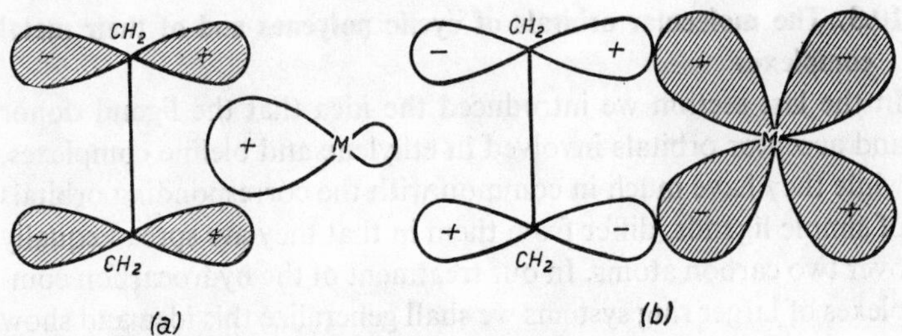

Fig. 10.2.2. Molecular orbitals for metal–olefine bonding. (a) The σ type orbital, (b) the π type orbital. The shaded orbitals are occupied and the unshaded orbitals unoccupied in the free metal ion and ligand

the ψ_A orbital on the olefine. This is the favourable situation which we discussed in Chapter 9, and can lead to more extensive bonding than would be anticipated from the donor or acceptor properties of olefines considered separately.

Acetylenes, unlike olefines, have doubly degenerate bonding and antibonding orbitals, ψ_A and ψ_B, which involve both the p_x

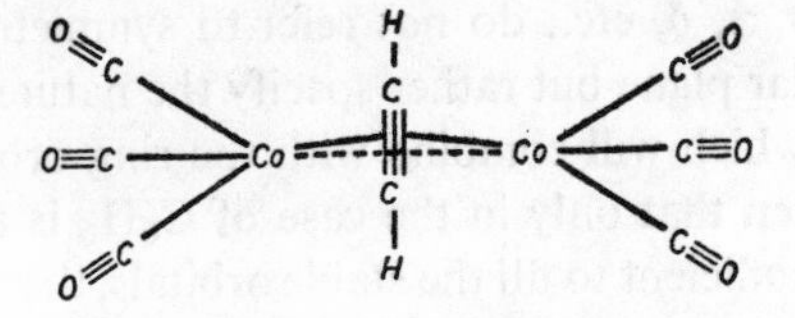

Fig. 10.2.3. The two metal–ligand bonds formed by acetylene in $(C_2H_2)Co_2(CO)_6$ *(diagrammatic)*

and p_y orbitals of the carbon atom. Consequently they can form two metal–ligand attachments roughly at right-angles to each other as shown in Fig. 10.2.3 for the particular case of an acetylene–cobalt carbonyl complex.

The presence of a metal ion on one side of an olefine or acetylene molecule in a complex can cause mixing of the σ and π orbitals of the olefine or acetylene. If this happens the CH bonds will bend back from the plane of the hydrocarbon molecule, away from the metal. (This is also true for the other hydrocarbon complexes.)

10.3. The molecular orbitals of cyclic polyenes and of their metal complexes

In the last section we introduced the idea that the ligand donor and acceptor orbitals involved in ethylene and olefine complexes, while they have much in common with the corresponding orbitals of simple ligands, differ from them in that they are spread equally over two carbon atoms. In our treatment of the hydrocarbon complexes of larger ring systems we shall generalize this idea and show how a complete molecular orbital, spread over a large number of carbon atoms, may also take part in bonding to a metal atom. As a preliminary to this we must say something about the orbitals of cyclic polyenes.

In Fig. 10.3.1 we give diagrams of the π molecular orbitals of each of the cyclic polyenes from C_3H_3 to C_8H_8. The energies of the corresponding molecular orbitals and their occupation numbers are given in Table 10.3.1.* In the diagrams we have classified the orbitals according to their symmetry with respect to a bond from the centre of the ring to an attached metal atom, that is, the designations σ, π, δ, etc., do not refer to symmetry with respect to the molecular plane but rather specify the nature of the orbital on the metal which will combine with the ring orbital.

It will be seen that only in the case of C_6H_6 is the number of electrons just sufficient to fill the stable orbitals, that is, the orbitals more stable than an orbital on a free carbon atom. In C_3H_3 and C_7H_7 one electron is obliged to go into an unstable orbital, and for this reason derivatives of the C_3H_3 and C_7H_7 ring systems are sometimes met as cations $C_3R_3^+$ and $C_7H_7^+$ which have lost this unstable electron. C_5H_5 has one vacancy in a stable molecular orbital and hence is often met with as an anion $C_5H_5^-$. The C_4H_4 ring, which has only recently been prepared,[1] has two elec-

* The constant β is the so-called exchange integral which plays an important part in the elementary molecular-orbital theory of conjugated hydrocarbons. Its value is uncertain, but of the order of 30 Kcals.

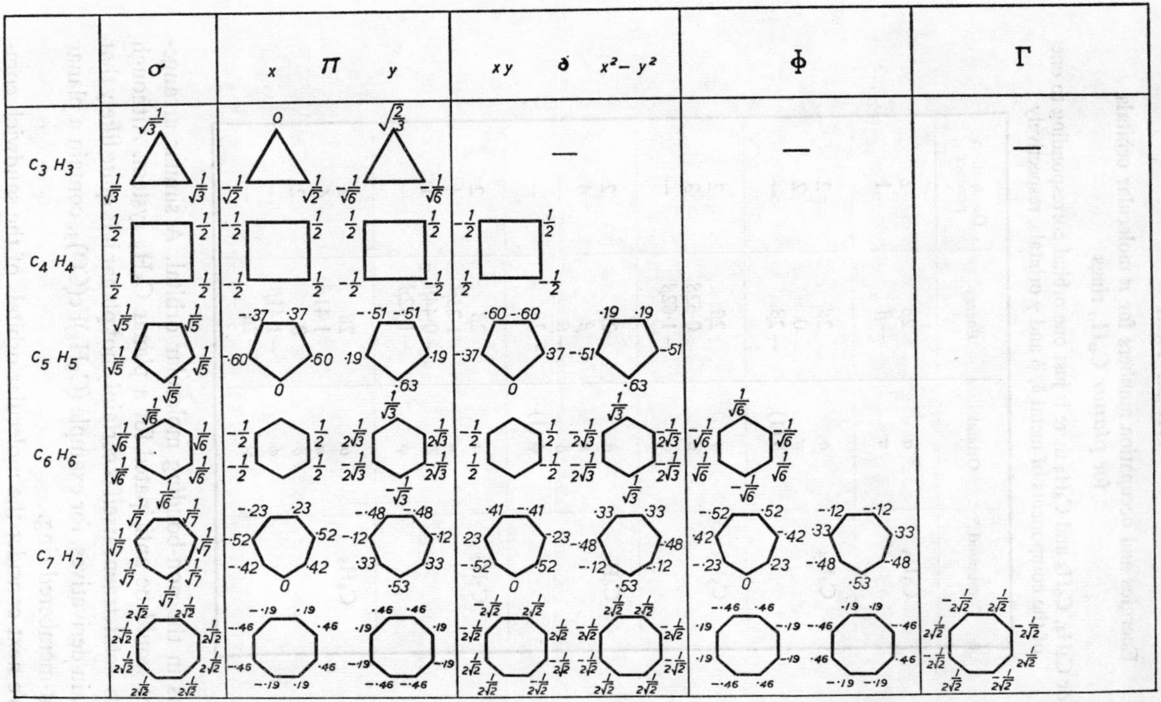

	σ	π (x)	π (y)	δ (xy)	δ (x^2-y^2)	Φ		Γ
C_3H_3				—		—		—
C_4H_4								
C_5H_5								
C_6H_6								
C_7H_7								
C_8H_8								

Fig. 10.3.1. *Molecular orbitals of cyclic polyenes. The coefficients of the individual atomic orbitals in each molecular orbital are given on the Figures*

TABLE 10.3.1

Energies and occupation numbers for π molecular orbitals for *planar* C_nH_n rings

For C_4H_4, C_6H_6 and C_8H_8 there is just one orbital corresponding to one of the components of metal δ, ϕ and γ orbitals, respectively

Compound	Orbital	Energy	Occupation number
C_3H_3	σ	2β	2
	π	$-\beta$	1
C_4H_4	σ	2β	2
	π	0	2
	δ (1)	-2β	—
C_5H_5	σ	2β	2
	π	$0{\cdot}62\beta$	3
	δ	$-1{\cdot}62\beta$	—
C_6H_6	σ	2β	2
	π	β	4
	δ	$-\beta$	—
	ϕ (1)	-2β	—
C_7H_7	σ	2β	2
	π	$1{\cdot}25\beta$	4
	δ	$-0{\cdot}44\beta$	1
	ϕ	$-1{\cdot}82\beta$	—
C_8H_8	σ	2β	2
	π	$1{\cdot}41\beta$	4
	δ	0	2
	ϕ	$-1{\cdot}41\beta$	—
	γ	-2β	—

trons in the non-bonding molecular orbital. A similar arrangement would be anticipated for a planar C_8H_8 system. Although cyclo-octatetraene itself is certainly not planar it is quite likely that certain derivatives, for example $(C_8H_8)Fe(CO)_3$, contain a planar eight-membered ring.

We next consider the molecular orbitals of the sandwich compounds in which a metal ion is placed between two similar rings as indicated in Fig. 10.1.1.*b* and *c*. For the moment we do not identify the particular cyclic polyene, since the theory is quite general. In the second column in Table 10.3.2 we classify the various

TABLE 10.3.2

The orbitals for sandwich molecules

Underlined orbitals are stable in the separate components. Asterisk denotes a doubly degenerate orbital

Group classification	Ring orbital	Metal orbital	Bonding orbital	Antibonding orbital
A_{1g}	$\underline{\sigma_g}$	$\underline{3d_{z^2}, 4s}$	2	1
A_{1u}	$\underline{\sigma_u}$	$4p_z$	1	1
E_{1g}	$\underline{\pi_g}$	$\underline{3d_{xz}, 3d_{yz}}$	1*	1*
E_{1u}	$\underline{\pi_u}$	$4p_x, 4p_y$	1*	1*
Only one component for C_4H_4 { E_{2g}	δ_g	$3d_{xy}, 3d_{x^2-y^2}$	1*	1*
E_{2u}	δ_u		Non-bonding and empty except perhaps in C_7H_7 and C_8H_8	

orbitals of the metal atom according to their σ, π or δ symmetry about the bond axis and according to their behaviour on inversion in the centre of symmetry at the metal atom. g signifies that an orbital is unchanged and u that it is changed in sign on inversion, for example the orbitals in Figs. 10.4.1 are all g, while p orbitals are all u.

From each type of orbital on the ring we get two orbitals, one g and one u—for example σ_g and σ_u from the σ orbitals on any of the ring systems. In column 3 of the table we give the metal orbitals with which the 2-ring molecular orbitals can combine. It should be noted that not all of these ring orbitals are available for each system. In C_3H_3, C_5H_5 and C_7H_7 the ring orbitals run up to π, δ and ϕ respectively. In C_4H_4 one component of a δ orbital is available, in C_6H_6 one component of a ϕ orbital, and in C_8H_8 one component of a γ orbital.

In columns 4 and 5 of the table we give the number of bonding and the number of antibonding combinations obtainable from the metal and ring orbitals of each kind. The ring ϕ and γ orbitals are of no interest since there are no metal orbitals to combine with them, and in the free hydrocarbons they are unstable and empty; they are therefore omitted from the table. Only in the case of the σ_g orbitals does any ambiguity concerning the number of stable orbitals arise, for it is not quite clear whether one or two orbitals should be stable. Theoretical arguments to be given in the next section suggest that the correct number is two, and this is certainly the number needed to explain the experimental data.

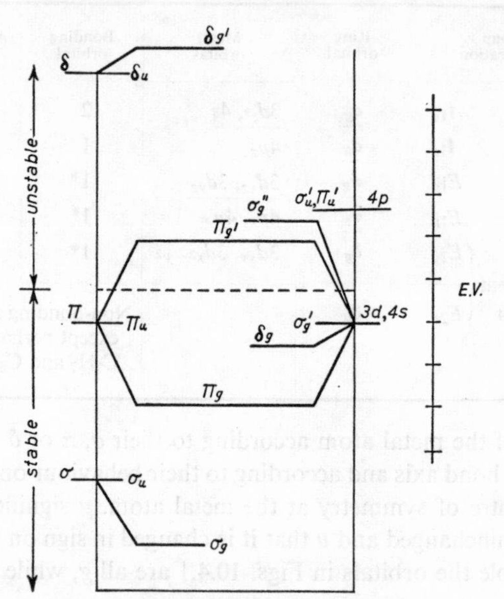

Fig. 10.3.2. Energy-level diagrams for the orbitals of ferrocene. Elsewhere we have designated orbitals by their group-theoretical classification symbols: $a = \sigma$, $e_1 = \pi$, $e_2 = \delta$

We next consider the number of stable orbitals that are available in the various sandwich molecules. For five-, six- and seven-membered rings there are just nine stable orbitals (cf. Section 9.7). These are roughly described as five stable metal 3*d* orbitals, more or less strongly combined with ligand *g* orbitals; three stable ligand *u* orbitals combined with unstable metal 4*p* orbitals, and finally a second stable σ_g orbital derived from the metal *s* orbital and the ligand σ_g orbital. (Actually this last orbital and the metal d_{z^2} orbital are mixed together.) Energy levels for the typical case of the metal dicyclopentadienyls are shown in Fig. 10.3.2. It should be noted that there is one stable orbital corresponding to each of the metal *s*, *p* and *d* orbitals, hence just enough room in stable orbitals for the eighteen electrons of the inert-gas structure.

In the C_3H_3 system the situation is somewhat different for the π orbital is relatively unstable and so, while the combination of the π_g orbital with metal *d* orbitals would be stable and occupied, the combination of the π_u orbital with the metal *p* orbital would probably be unoccupied. Thus C_3H_3 will probably have complexing characteristics quite different from those of the larger ring systems. It should be analogous in many ways to nitric oxide, filling one coordination place on the metal but supplying two σ and one π electron. No compounds of C_3H_3 are at present known but $(C_3H_3)PtCl_3$, $(C_3H_3)Co(CO)_3$ and $(C_3H_3)CuCl$ might be expected to exist. We do not discuss C_8H_8 in detail since little is known about C_8H_8 sandwich compounds and the theory is a little complicated.

10.4. Particular metal-cyclic polyene compounds

(*a*) *Eight-membered rings*

Cyclo-octatetraene itself is not planar but has a 'tub' configuration. Infra-red and nuclear resonance evidence has recently been presented suggesting that, in the compound $C_8H_8Fe(CO)_3$, the ring may have the planar configuration.[2]

(*b*) *Seven-membered rings*

Only a very few compounds of the C_7H_7 radical are known. Of these the most interesting are the salts of the $[(C_7H_7)Mo(CO)_3]^+$ cation. They are diamagnetic, the ion having the 'inert-gas' configuration with eighteen valence electrons. (The isoelectronic molecules $(C_6H_6)Co(CO)_3$ and $(C_5H_5)Mn(CO)_3$ are also known.)

(*c*) *Six-membered rings*

The first neutral compound of benzene to be prepared was $Cr(C_6H_6)_2$. This is a diamagnetic solid with eighteen valence electrons. Reference to Fig. 10.3.2, which gives the correct occupied levels for dibenzenes but which is otherwise not applicable even semi-quantitatively, shows that if all stable orbitals are to be used the six d electrons must be paired in the d_{z^2}, d_{xy} and $d_{x^2-y^2}$ (σ_g, δ_g) orbitals since the stable π_g orbitals are occupied by ligand electrons. Hence the diamagnetism of the compound. The bonding is rather similar to that in the olefine complexes, but now the top occupied orbital of the ligand is of the π type and electrons are donated from it into the d_{xz} and d_{yz} orbitals of the metal. The first empty orbitals of the ligands are the δ type orbitals, and these

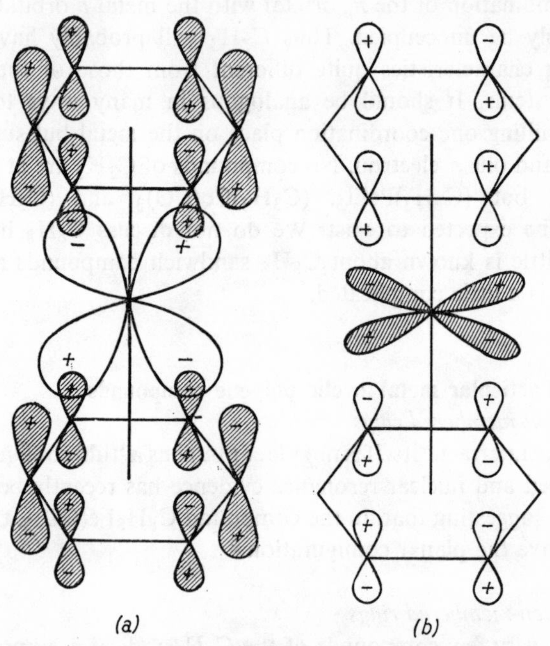

Fig. 10.4.1. Bonding orbitals for $Cr(C_6H_6)_2$. *(a) The x component of the degenerate π bonding orbital, (b) the xy component of the degenerate δ bonding orbital. Shaded orbitals occupied in metal and ligand*

must accept electrons from the filled $d_{x^2-y^2}$ and d_{xy} orbitals of the metal. These combined orbitals are shown in Fig. 10.4.1. Again we have a saturated molecule attached to a metal atom by simultaneous donor and acceptor action, though orbitals of different symmetry, π and δ this time, are used instead of σ and π as with CO and olefines.

The alternative description of double-donor action which we have given for metal carbonyls is quite instructive here. We note that the first excited state of benzene, about 4 e.v. above the ground state, is a triplet state of the configuration $\sigma^2\pi^3\delta^1$. This can combine strongly with a metal atom having two unpaired electrons, one in a π and the other in a δ orbital. The two-way coordination suggested above is equivalent to mixing some of the wave-function of this strongly bonded excited structure with the wave-function based on the ground state of the benzene molecule.

(*d*) *Five-membered rings*

By now some hundreds of derivatives in which a metal is joined by a sandwich bond to one or more cyclopentadienyl rings are

TABLE 10.4.1

Some compounds containing 'sandwich-bonded' cyclopentadienyl radicals

Molecules marked with an asterisk have one or more unpaired electrons

Type of compound	Examples	Remarks
Metal bis-cyclopentadienyl	$M(C_5H_5)_2$ M = Ti, V*, Cr*, Mn*, Fe, Co*, Ni*; Ru; Os; Mg	
Metal bis-cyclopentadienyl cations	$[M(C_5H_5)_2]^+$ M = Ti*, V*, Cr*, Fe*, Co; Ru*, Rh; Ir $[M(C_5H_5)_2]^{2+}$ M = Ti, V*; Zr	'Covalent' derivatives of many of these ions are known
Mixed cyclopentadiene carbonyls and nitrosyls	$(C_5H_5)V(CO)_4$; $(C_5H_5)Mn(CO)_3$ $(C_5H_5)Co(CO)_2$, $(C_5H_5)Ni(NO)$ $[(C_5H_5)_2Fe(CO)_2]_2$, $[(C_5H_5)Mo(CO)_3]_2$, $(C_5H_5)_3Ni_3(CO)_2$*	Many more compounds have been described
Hydrides and alkyls	$(C_5H_5)_2ReH$, $(C_5H_5)Cr(CO)_3CH_3$	
Mixed sandwiches	$(C_5H_4.CH_3)Mn(C_6H_6)$, $(C_6H_6)Cr(C_5H_5)$ * $[C_6H_3(CH_3)_3Fe(C_5H_5)]^+$	

known. We cannot deal here with the organic chemistry of ferrocene, for while this is of the greatest interest it involves problems and methods rather different from those with which we are concerned. In Table 10.4.1 we list a few of the more interesting mixed cyclopentadienyls, containing carbon monoxide, nitric oxide, etc., as ligands. It will be noted that in almost every case the inert-gas number of electrons is achieved, occasionally by dimerization as in the compound $(C_5H_5)_2Mo_2(CO)_6$. Some of the more interesting structures which have been established are illustrated in Fig. 10.4.2.

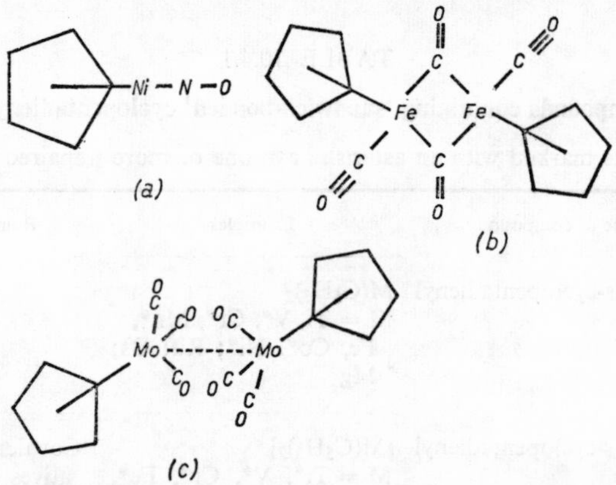

Fig. 10.4.2. The structure of some simple mixed cyclopentadienyl metal compounds. (*a*) $(C_5H_5)Ni(No)$, (*b*) $(C_5H_5)_2Fe_2(CO)_4$, (*c*) $(C_5H_5)_2Mo_2(CO)_6$

The bis-cyclopentadienyls of all of the elements from titanium to nickel have been prepared and their properties recorded. It is these which we shall discuss in detail, although our remarks, with important quantitative modifications in certain cases, should also apply to cations $[M(C_5H_5)_2]^{n+}$ and to the cyclopentadienyls of the metals of the second and third transition series.

The fact that the Mg^{2+} ion forms a bis-cyclopentadienyl which has the same molecular structure as the transition-metal compounds indicates quite clearly that the stereochemistry of the group of compounds does not require an explanation involving *d* electron bonding. The structure of the magnesium compound probably represents the most favourable way of packing together $(C_5H_5)^-$ groups, in which the electric charge is evenly spread over the carbon atoms of the ring, and Mg^{2+} ions. Certainly the structure in which the Mg^{2+} ion is close to a particular carbon atom carrying a unit negative charge would be more favourable electrostatically, but the energy required to localize such a charge on the ring would be large. As with octahedral complexes, the basic molecular structure of transition-metal cyclopentadienyls is of a kind which is consistent both with electrostatic and with covalent bonding. We have to discuss the electronic structure, in particular the behaviour of the *d* electrons, in the light of the given geometrical configuration. The degree of delocalization of *d* electrons can be determined by magnetic resonance experiments, or inferred indirectly from other properties.

The semi-empirical energy-level diagram for the bis-cyclopentadienyl compounds is shown in Fig. 10.3.2. For the moment we concentrate on the description of $Fe(C_5H_5)_2$, the most stable and by far the least labile member of the series. The σ_g, σ_u and π_u orbitals, mainly concentrated on the rings, and the d_{z^2}, $d_{x^2-y^2}$ and d_{xy} orbitals, mainely on the metal, are all fully occupied and together contain fourten electrons. The remaining four electrons occupy the π_g orbital, which is strongly bonding and fairly equally distributed over the metal and the ring. We can describe this situation qualitatively in the following way: the iron atom is prepared in the configuration $(d_{x^2-y^2})^2(d_{xy})^2(d_{z^2})^2(d_{xz})^1(d_{yz})^1$, the pair of cyclopentadienyl rings in the complementary configuration $(\sigma_g)^2(\sigma_u)^2(\pi_u)^4(\pi_{gx})^1(\pi_{gy})^1$, and the two are brought together with the formation of two *covalent* single bonds by pairing the d_{xz} and d_{yz} orbitals, on the one hand, with the π_{gx} and π_{gy} orbitals on the other. The critical bonding orbital is shown in Fig. 10.4.3 and the effect of bonding in the energy-level diagram in Fig. 10.3.2 where the two π_g orbitals are shown to split wide apart.

In addition to these bonds a variety of subsidiary ones are formed, just as we found for $Cr(C_6H_6)_2$, etc. Many different views have been expressed as to the relative importance of the different types of bonding, some believing that only the π_g orbitals of the ring are important and others attributing great importance to the other orbitals of the metal. This point is a quantitative one, and has not been settled. It does, however, seem unlikely that the subsidiary bonds can be ignored, since in chromium dibenzene

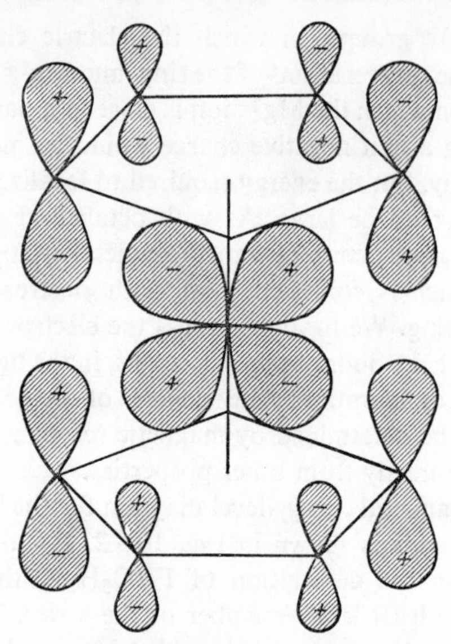

Fig. 10.4.3. One component of the critical π bonding orbital in ferrocene

there are no unpaired electrons on the benzene rings, and hence all the bonding must be of the type of the subsidiary bonding in ferrocene. We have indicated a certain measure of subsidiary bonding in our energy-level diagram, but this diagram is not *quantitative.*

We must now turn to important matters of detail. Moffitt has pointed out that the mixing of the metal $3d_{z^2}$ and $4s$ orbitals in ferrocene has an important effect on the bonding. The orbital $\frac{1}{\sqrt{2}}(3d_{z^2} + 4s)$ has very high density close to the rings, while the combination $\frac{1}{\sqrt{2}}(3d_{z^2} - 4s)$ is a disc-like orbital parallel to the rings (cf. Fig. 4.5.1). Thus an unshared pair of metal electrons in the latter orbital is removed from the neighbourhood of the rings and hence stabilized substantially. The remaining combination of d_{z^2} and s orbitals is an orbital which strongly overlaps the filled σ_g orbital of the rings and can form a partial bond with it. Thus there are two stable σ_g orbitals. Moffitt further suggests that this interaction of the $4s$ with the $3d_{z^2}$ orbital pushes down the latter until it is substantially below the $d_{x^2-y^2}$ and d_{xy} orbitals. This, as we shall see, is important in any discussion of the magnetic properties of these compounds.

The magnetic moments of the cyclopentadienyls are given in Table 10.4.2. $Co(C_5H_5)_2$ has one more electron than $Fe(C_5H_5)_2$

TABLE 10.4.2

Magnetic moments and number of unpaired spins of bis-cyclopentadienyls

Metal ion	Number of *d* electrons	Magnetic moment (Bohr magnetons)	Number of unpaired electrons
Ti^{3+}	1	2·3	1
V^{4+} (dichloride)	1	1·95	1
Ti^{2+}	2	0	0
V^{3+}	2	2·86±0·6	2
V^{2+}	3	3·78±0·19	3
Cr^{3+}	3	3·81	3
Cr^{2+}	4	3·02±0·15	2
Mn^{2+}	5	(5·9) ??	5
Fe^{3+}	5	2·26	1
Fe^{2+}	6	0	0
Co^{3+}	6	0	0
Co^{2+}	7	1·76±0·07	1
Ni^{2+}	8	2·86±0·1	2

and this we believe occupies the antibonding π_g orbital, thus reducing the bond strength considerably. The two extra electrons in $Ni(C_5H_5)_2$ probably enter this same double degenerate orbital with their spins parallel. These assignments are consistent with the magnetic evidence. Other arguments in their favour are the experimentally observed increase in the metal–carbon bond length as one goes from $Fe(C_5H_5)_2$ to $Ni(C_5H_5)_2$, the thermodynamic data, a detailed interpretation of the visible spectrum of $Ni(C_5H_5)_2$,[3] and the analogy with octahedral complexes which we shall develop later.

At the beginning of the series the two 'non-bonding' electrons of $Ti(C_5H_5)_2$ are paired as shown by the diamagnetism of this compound. Hence the non-degenerate d_{z^2} orbital must be substantially below the $d_{x^2-y^2}$ and d_{xy} orbitals, for if one or both *d* electrons were in the latter we should have a triplet ground state.

However, in $V(C_5H_5)_2$ we find three unpaired electrons, not one as might perhaps have been expected. The reason for this is now clear, namely that the loss of exchange energy is roughly K for spin-pairing a d^2 compound but amounts to $2K$ for a d^3 compound* (cf. the arguments of Chapter 3). The electronic structure of $Cr(C_5H_5)_2$ follows the same pattern. The configuration must be $(d_{z^2})^2(d_{xz}, d_{yz})^2$ to account for the two unpaired electrons. With $Mn(C_5H_5)_2$, however, we find a structure of another kind, namely one with five unpaired electrons. There can be little doubt that the electron configuration is $(d_{z^2})^1(d_{x^2-y^2}, d_{xy})^2(\pi_g)^2$, and that owing to the large exchange energy of the high-spin d^5 configuration two electrons have been forced into the antibonding π_g orbital, thus weakening the bond by about as much as in $Ni(C_5H_5)_2$.

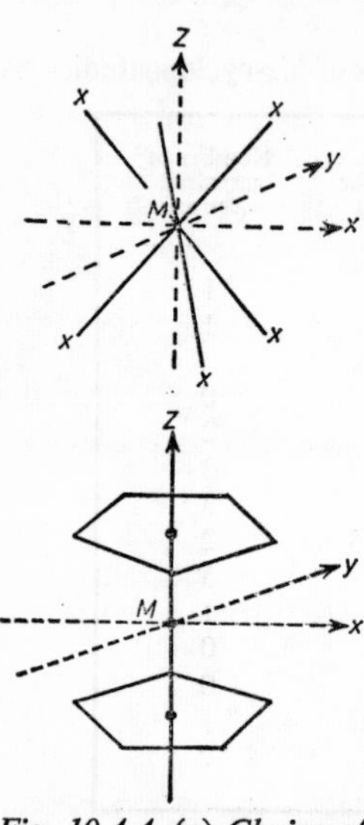

Fig. 10.4.4. (a) Choice of axes for referring d orbitals to a three-fold axis of an octahedral complex, (b) ferrocene – to show similarity of choice of axes to (a)

The closeness of the analogy between the magnetic and other properties of these compounds and those of certain octahedral complexes supports these electron assignments. Thus one may compare the cyclopentadienyls, considered as derivatives of a $(C_5H_5)^-$ anion, with the phenanthrolines and note that in both cases the 'ligand-field enforces spin-pairing for Fe^{2+} and Co^{2+} but not for Mn^{2+}. (The analogy goes further for $[Fe(C_5H_5)_2]^+$ like $[Fe(Phe)_3]^{3+}$ is spin-paired although isoelectronic $(MnC_5H_5)_2$ and $[Mn(Phe)_3]^{2+}$ are high-spin compounds.)

These remarks lead in a natural way to what I believe to be the explanation of the frequently noted resemblance between biscyclopentadienyls and dibenzenes on the one hand and octahedral complexes on the other. Consider an octahedral complex of the usual kind, but in order to facilitate comparison with the ring

* This places quite definite limits on the energy separation between the d_{z^2} orbital and the $d_{x^2-y^2}$ and d_{xy} orbitals.

systems, redefine the d orbitals with respect to a three-fold axis as shown in Fig. 10.4.4. There are of course just three stable t_{2g} and two less stable e_g orbitals as before, but now we must write them as

$$\left.\begin{matrix} d_{z^2} \\ \sqrt{\tfrac{2}{3}}d_{x^2-y^2}+\sqrt{\tfrac{1}{3}}d_{xz} \\ \sqrt{\tfrac{2}{3}}d_{xy}-\sqrt{\tfrac{1}{3}}d_{yz} \end{matrix}\right\}t_{2g} \quad \left.\begin{matrix} \sqrt{\tfrac{1}{3}}d_{x^2-y^2}-\sqrt{\tfrac{2}{3}}d_{xz} \\ \sqrt{\tfrac{1}{3}}d_{xy}+\sqrt{\tfrac{2}{3}}d_{yz} \end{matrix}\right\}e_g$$

If we distort the octahedron somewhat, by flattening, without removing the three-fold axis we get the energy-level pattern shown in Fig. 10.4.5. An appropriate distortion will in fact produce an

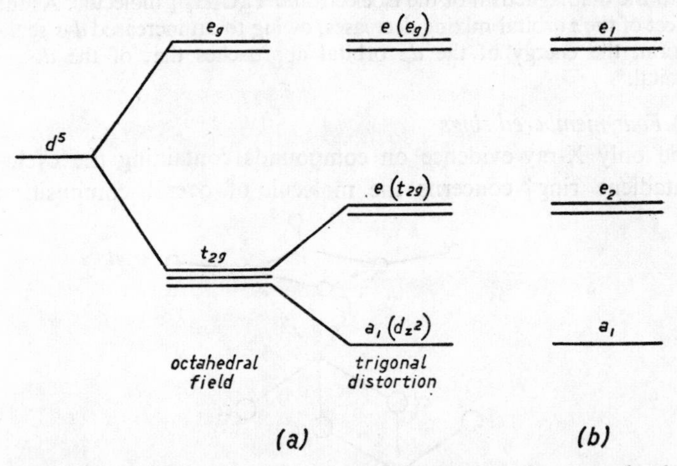

Fig. 10.4.5. (*a*) *The effect of a trigonal distortion on the energy levels of an octahedral complex.* (*b*) *The 'd orbital' energy levels for ferrocene*

energy-level diagram almost identical with that for bis-cyclopentadienyls, and even without distortion the resemblance, apart from the degeneracy of the d_{z^2} and the other two t_{2g} orbitals, is striking.

The arguments which we have used before show that qualitatively the properties of a series of transition-metal compounds are more closely connected with the nature of the orbitals and the pattern of energy levels than with the mechanisms responsible for producing that pattern. Thus provided, quite formally and without any implication about the nature of the bonds, we consider the cyclopentadienyls as derivatives of the $(C_5H_5)^-$ ion, most of the arguments given for octahedral complexes apply with slight modification also to cyclopentadienyls. We cannot go into detail here, but suffice it to say we may expect Jahn–Teller effects for spin-paired d^7 ions, e.g. $Co(C_5H_5)_2$, non-lability for d^6 compounds, in particular $Fe(C_5H_5)_2$, etc.

The relative positions of the d_{z^2} orbital and the $d_{x^2-y^2}$ and d_{xy} orbitals is of considerable interest in connexion with the detailed optical and magnetic properties of the cyclopentadienyls. It may be anticipated that while $3d_{z^2} - 4s$ mixing is important in the neutral molecules, it will be less so in the cations $[M(C_5H_5)_2]^+$ since the *d–s* separation increases rapidly with the charge on the metal ion. In agreement with this is the paramagnetism of the $[V(C_5H_5)_2]^+$ ion, which contrasts with the diamagnetism of the isoelectronic $Ti(C_5H_5)_2$ molecule. As the effect of the *s* orbital mixing decreases, owing to an increased *d–s* separation, the energy of the d_{z^2} orbital approaches that of the $d_{x^2-y^2}$ orbital.*

(*e*) *Four-membered rings*

The only X-ray evidence on compounds containing the cyclobutadiene ring† concerns the molecule of overall composition

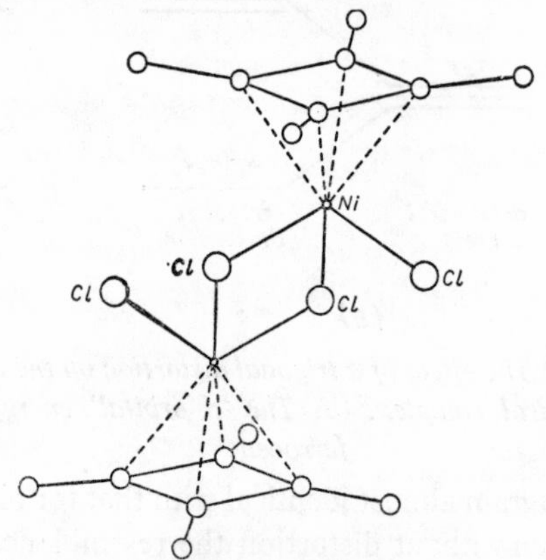

Fig. 10.4.6. The structure of $(C_4Me_4)_2Ni_2Cl_4$

(Dunitz, private communication)

* However, recent theoretical calculations make it surprising that the $Ti(C_5H_5)_2$ is diamagnetic.[3] Further experiments to check that the observed diamagnetism is not due to dimerization or antiferromagnetic interaction between molecules would be most valuable.

† A second X-ray structure, that of tetraphenyl cyclobutadiene iron tricarbonyl has now been determined (Schomaker, *Nature*, in press, 1960).

$C_4Me_4NiCl_2$.[4] In fact this molecule is a dimer having the structure shown in Fig. 10.4.6. The participation of the closely related $[(C_4H_4)Ni(CN)_2]$ molecule in Reppe's cyclo-octatetraene synthesis was postulated some time ago, but it is still not known whether the reaction involves cyclobutadiene derivatives.

$[(C_4Me_4NiCl_2]_2$ provided the first example of an otherwise unknown hydrocarbon being made stable by combination with a metal ion. A number of other unusual hydrocarbon fragments may be capable of existence in association with an appropriate configuration of metal atoms or ions.

10.5. Other metal–hydrocarbon coordination compounds

Among the simplest of the remaining hydrocarbon derivatives of the metals are the butadiene derivatives of iron carbonyl having the general formula $RFe(CO)_3$ where R can be almost any simple butadiene derivative. The fact that 1,3-cyclohexadiene forms such a compound makes it probable that the structure is as shown in Fig. 10.5.1. The filled orbitals of the diene provide just four electrons to complete the inert-gas structure of the $Fe(CO)_3$ radical. Double-bonding using the empty π orbitals of the ligand is also possible. The group $Fe(CO)_3$, indeed, has many of the

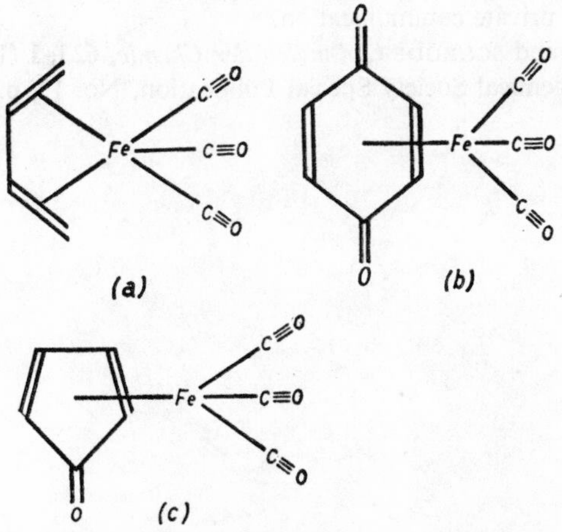

(a)

(b)

(c)

Fig. 10.5.1. The proposed structures of (a) $(C_4H_6)Fe(CO)_3$, *(b)* $(C_6H_4O_2)Fe(CO)_3$, *(c)* $(C_5H_4O)Fe(CO)_3$

characteristics of a dienophile, forming compounds also with *p*-quinones and with cyclopentadienone (Fig. 10.5.1*b–c*).

A considerable number of transition-metal acetylides are now known. They are quite different from the sandwich molecules and from the alkyls. They may perhaps be compared most profitably with the corresponding cyanides, for example $[Fe(CN)_6]^{4-}$ with $[Fe(C{\equiv}CR)_6]^{4-}$, etc.[5]

CHAPTER TEN

REVIEW REFERENCES

COTTON and WILKINSON, *Progress in Inorganic Chemistry*, Vol. I, p. 1 (1959)

FISCHER and FRITZ, *Advances in Inorganic Chemistry and Radiochemistry*, Vol. 1, p. 55. Academic Press, New York, 1959

Also a series of papers in Chemical Society Special Publication No. 13, 1959. (Report on International Conference in Co-ordination Chemistry)

1. ARRAN, MORICA and NENITZESCU, *Berichte*, **92,** 1088 (1959)
2. RAUSCH and SCHRAUZER, *Chem. and Industry*, 957 (1959)
3. LEVY, unpublished results
4. DUNITZ, private communication.
   CRIEGEE and SCHRÖDER, *Annalen der Chemie*, **623,** 1 (1959)
5. NAST, Chemical Society Special Publication, No. 13, p. 103 (1959)

CHAPTER ELEVEN

The Highest Valencies of the Transition Metals

11.1. Octahedral compounds

The highest oxidation states of the transition metals are almost always exhibited in their oxides and fluorides, although a few interesting coordination compounds of metal ions in high valencies with arsines, etc., are known. In these compounds the degree of covalency must be large. Sometimes the mixing of metal *d* orbitals with other metal orbitals and with ligand orbitals is so extensive that the electrostatic approach is of little value and a full-scale molecular-orbital description is essential, but in octahedral compounds the ligand-field method which hypothesizes predominantly d^n electron configurations for the metal ion is still useful.

As an example of a set of compounds to which simple methods may be applied we take the group of volatile hexafluorides WF_6, ReF_6, OsF_6, IrF_6 and PtF_6. In WF_6 the metal may be regarded as making six metal–ligand bonds of the usual sort, using the molecular orbitals derived from metal $d(e_g)$, *s* and *p* orbitals. In the remaining compounds σ bonds are formed in the same way and one to four electrons are added to the t_{2g} orbital, thus giving the low-spin complex in the case of PtF_6.

The spectra of all these compounds are capable of a detailed interpretation in terms of a single parameter,[1] the spin-orbit coupling constant, since the ligand-field splitting Δ is not involved in the calculation of the energies of transitions within a $(t_{2g})^n$ configuration and the spectra are due to such transitions.*

* The spin-orbit coupling increases rapidly with the atomic number of an ion and tends to determine the main features of the electronic structure of complexes of metals of the heaviest transition series. Of course, one also needs other information about the levels of the *free* ions in making these calculations

The ligand-field theory applies here as well as to any set of metal compounds of lower valency. The reason for this success is perhaps that the property which we are examining depends largely on the behaviour of the t_{2g} orbitals, and these are less extensively involved in π bonding than are the antibonding e_g orbitals in σ bonding.

It seems that octahedrally coordinated compounds of the metals in their highest valencies are almost always of the low-spin type. This is to be expected since ligand-fields increase rapidly with the valency of the metal ion and electron repulsion parameters are decreased through extensive delocalization. Thus $LiNiO_2$ is one of the few low-spin d^7 complexes.[2] The properties of compounds containing octahedrally coordinated ions of high valency fit quite well with a simple ligand-field theory based on well-defined d^n configurations for metal ions provided the restriction to low-spin configurations is recalled.

11.2. Tetrahedrally coordinated oxides of high valency

In the octahedral transition-metal oxides such as ReO_3 or the volatile fluorides such as PtF_6 we have seen that a formal description in which a definite number of *d* electrons are assigned to the t_{2g} orbitals proves useful in interpreting spectra and magnetic properties. Of course the e_g orbitals are extensively involved in bonding, but this does not affect the usefulness of the ligand-field description. In the tetrahedral complexes of high valency ions the ligand-field approach has not yet proved as useful.

In tetrahedral complexes the *t* orbitals, which are involved in both σ and π bonding, and the *e* orbitals, which take part only in π bonding, seem to be extensively delocalized. This leads to such serious difficulties in determining the energy levels that it is still not entirely clear whether the first *d* electron added to the MnO_4^- ion or to related ions enters an *e* or a t_2 orbital.

This difficulty may be in part due to the fact that the metal ions in the tetrahedral compounds which have been investigated carefully are in *very* high oxidation states so that the compounds must be very covalent in character. Again, extensive delocalization is favoured by the small number of ligands; electroneutrality can hardly be achieved by transfer of σ electrons alone in an ion like MnO_4^-, since it is unlikely that almost two electrons could be removed from the $p\sigma$ orbital of each O^{2-} ion. This means that the π orbitals are used more extensively in bonding than they are, say, in an octahedrally coordinated compound of W^{6+}. Yet another complication is the extensive *d–p* mixing which occurs in tetrahedral complexes, and which makes it doubtful whether any theory based on almost pure d^n configurations can be adequate.

The consequence of these difficulties is that no simple theory of the magnetic and optical properties of these tetrahedral complexes yet exists. It is to be hoped that the work which is just beginning on the optical absorption and paramagnetic resonance spectra of ions such as $(MnO_4)^{2-}$ and $(FeO_4)^{2-}$ will establish how far simple molecular-orbital theory will suffice to give a semi-quantitative description of the ground and excited electronic states.[3] *

A detailed theory of the optical absorption spectrum of the MnO_4^- ion and isoelectronic ions has been given.[4, 5] The transitions involved are not very closely related to *d–d* transitions (formally, in an electrostatic theory, there are no *d* electrons), but correspond to the transfer of electrons between delocalized molecular orbitals. They have more in common with the charge-transfer spectra of octahedral complexes than with the *d–d* transitions. This perhaps is the reason for much greater intensity of the longest wave-length bands of MnO_4^-, for example, than of those of octahedral complexes.

11.3. Stereochemistry of high-valency oxides

The lower oxides of the transition metals almost all have structures based on octahedral coordination, while the highest oxides of these elements are often tetrahedrally coordinated. Thus the Mn^{6+} and Mn^{7+} ions in MnO_4^{2-} and MnO_4^- are tetrahedrally coordinated. In the first short period, oxides of ions of valency four or less are usually octahedrally coordinated and those of six- and seven-valent ions are often tetrahedrally coordinated.

In the later transition series the range of stability of the octahedral configuration extends further, presumably on account of

* This expectation has now been realized. See *Proc. Roy. Soc., A* **254,** 101 (1960), and references therein.

the larger size of the metal ions. Nb^{5+}, Ta^{6+}, Mo^{6+} and W^{6+} have all been found in more or less regular octahedral environments, but W^{6+} and particularly Mo^{6+} also occur frequently in tetrahedral environments.

The ions with radii such that the octahedral and tetrahedral oxide ion environments are of comparable stability often form oxides with very unusual structures. Thus in V_2O_5 the metal ion is surrounded by so irregular an octahedron of oxide ions that it is usually regarded as five-coordinated (Fig. 11.3.1). In other V^{5+} compounds the metal ion is sometimes tetrahedrally coordinated and sometimes occurs in environments of very low symmetry, often five-coordinated.

A detailed examination of the structures of a variety of Mo^{6+}, W^{6+}, Nb^{5+} and Ta^{5+} compounds reveals a quite general tendency for the octahedral environment of the metal to be irregular. The observed structures can often be derived from regular octahedrally coordinated structures by displacement of the metal ion from the centre of an oxide octahedron with only minor displacements of the oxide ions themselves. It is even possible to discern a gradually increasing tendency to deviate from regular octahedral symmetry in the series of ions:

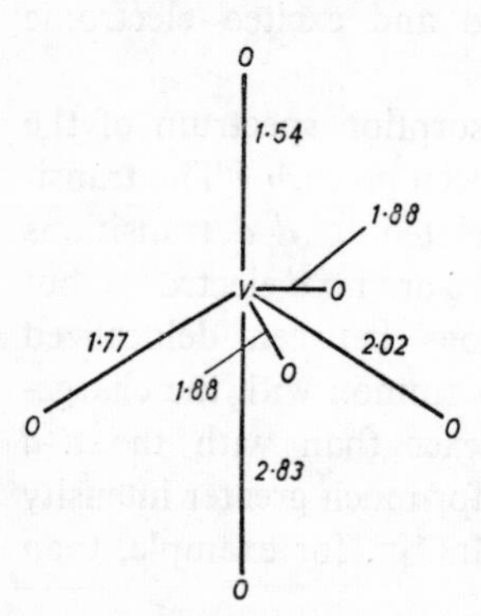

Fig. 11.3.1. The environment of the V^{5+} *ion in* V_2O_5

Hf^{4+}, Zr^{4+}, Ti^{4+}, Nb^{5+}, Ta^{5+}, W^{6+}, Mo^{6+}, V^{5+}, Cr^{6+}, Mn^{7+}.

This is, roughly speaking, the order of decreasing ionic size, and so it has been suggested that distorted octahedral structures occur for metal ions which are too small to form regular octahedrally coordinated oxides, but are not small enough to be restricted to tetrahedrally coordinated structures. The metal ions 'rattle' inside an octahedron of oxide ions.[6]

Whether or not this is the correct explanation of the stereochemical facts the consequences of this tendency to distort are important. The useful properties of $BaTiO_3$ and other perovskites, the largest and one of the most important classes of ferroelectric material, are in part the consequence of this instability of the higher oxides to distortion. It has been suggested, also, that the curious cage structures of the heteropolymolybdates and heteropolytungstates are controlled by the tendency to distort of regular MoO_6 and WO_6 groups.[7] Certainly it is possible to understand why the higher oxides of the *A* sub-group elements form complex anions the structures of which are specific for the metal concerned if the differing tendencies of the metal ions to distortion are recalled.

CHAPTER ELEVEN

REFERENCES

1. MOFFITT, GOODMAN, FRED and WEINSTOCK, *Molecular Physics*, **2,** 109 (1959)
2. BONGERS, Thesis, Leyden, 1957
3. CARRINGTON, SCHONLAND and SYMONS, *J. Chem. Soc.*, 659 (1957), and references therein
4. WOLFSBERG and HELMHOLZ, *J. Chem. Phys.*, **20,** 837 (1952)
5. LIEHR and BALLHAUSEN, *J. Molec. Spectrosc.*, **2,** 342 (1958)
6. ORGEL, *Faraday Society Discussion*, **No. 26,** 138 (1958)
7. VAN ARKEL, private communication

Appendix

THE MAGNETIC SUSCEPTIBILITIES OF TRANSITION-METAL COMPOUNDS

The calculation of the paramagnetic susceptibility of a compound involves two steps. First we must find the size of its magnetic moment and then we must derive a relationship between the moment and the susceptibility. Here we give only a qualitative discussion. We do not deal with diamagnetic susceptibility, except to remark that nearly all compounds without unpaired electrons are diamagnetic.

The essential physical idea relating the magnetic moment to the susceptibility is that in a magnetic field the moments tend to align parallel to the field, but are prevented from achieving more than a very partial alignment by the thermal motion (except in very high fields at very low temperatures). The susceptibility χ is proportional to the degree of alignment and so is clearly going to increase with μ and decrease with T. Theory shows that

$$\chi = \frac{\mu^2}{3kT}.$$

There are two contributions to μ, the paramagnetic moment of a free atom; one arises from the spins of the electrons and the other from their orbital motion. The way in which these partial moments couple together is quite complicated. Fortunately in transition-metal *compounds* the orbital motion of electrons is severely restricted by the less than spherically symmetrical environment and so we can usually neglect all but the spin contribution to the moment. An essentially quantum-mechanical argument shows that the magnetic moment for a system of n unpaired electrons is

$$\mu = 2\sqrt{S(S+1)}\,\mu_0 = \sqrt{n(n+2)}\,\mu_0$$

where $\mu_0 = \frac{eh}{4\pi mc}$ is called the Bohr magneton.* This formula, together with that given in the last paragraph, provides a direct link between the measured magnetic susceptibility and the number of unpaired electrons.

While the orbital motion of the electrons is severely hindered (quenched) by the field due to the environment in most compounds its contribution to the magnetic moment of a complex is not always negligible. Pauling seems to have been the first to have realized that the size of the small orbital contributions to the magnetic moment can give clues to the nature of the environment of a metal ion.[1] More recently this idea has been applied more extensively, particularly by Nyholm.[2] It is very useful, for example, in distinguishing tetrahedral from octahedral complexes of Co^{2+} and Ni^{2+}.

The spin-only formula for the magnetic moment is adequate only so long as the splitting due to spin-orbit coupling is small compared with thermal energies (kT). Thus there are serious deviations from the predictions of the simple theory for complexes of metals of the later transition series at room temperature, and even for compounds of Ti^{3+}, etc., at sufficiently low temperatures.

APPENDIX

REFERENCES

1. PAULING, *The Nature of the Chemical Bond*, 2nd edition. Oxford University Press, 1940, p. 121
2. NYHOLM, *Quart. Rev.*, **7**, 377 (1953)

* In a classical theory one would expect the moment for n electrons to be given by the relation

$$\mu = n\mu_0 = 2S\mu_0.$$

This is not correct, essentially because the orientation of the spin in quantum theory is not so well defined as in the classical theory.

Index